PRAISE FOR AL[illegible]IETNAM

I am so moved by the emotional and cultural honesty written in every page of this book that are both personal and universal to the Vietnamese-American experience. As a Child and Adolescent psychiatrist, I appreciated the balance in perspectives of both the main character, Anh, and her mother, Xuan. As a former refugee from Vietnam, I just cried for the mother 's and daughter's aching longings--for a culture, a place, a past, a future, a family, a home that could only exist in their memories and dreams. I didn't want Anh's journey to end.

- Kiet Truong, MD, Child and Adolescent Psychiatrist

Powered by story and strengthened by science, Dr. Elizabeth Nguyen, like Lisa Genova before her, has penned a gripping story of one family's journey through the heartbreak of mental illness. A beautifully written coming-of-age story that details the highs and lows of bipolar disorder, against the cross-cultural grace and beauty of two Pacific locations – Vietnam and Hawaii. A poignant and moving novel.

- R. Bruce Logan & Elaine Head,
authors of *Back to Vietnam: Tours of the Heart*

Edge of your seat fixed reading: as soon as I settled with "Aloha Vietnam," I was hooked on the raw emotion pouring deep from within the words. The pace of the story is perfect and it takes no time to feel connected to each of the characters. Elizabeth's passion for her cultural roots bursts throughout this poignant encounter of a family both found and lost within their new experiences. I loved it.

- Natalie Farrell, Artist. Presenter.
Writer + Author of *Light The Way*

This beautiful book tenderly pulls you into the pages, sharing the insights of a mother and daughter, both raised and managing their lives through two different cultures, loss, a mental health diagnosis and treatment. At the heart of this story, you are taken on a journey of the two women conveying resilience, strength, and hope to be found from the confusion, uncertainty, and mental health that arise within both of their worlds. I found myself transported into a world of fragility, tenderness, and hope, held by the exploration of painting and the power of the sea. This enchanting book is a potent mix of loss, strength, love, and healing.

- Deborah DLP, Writer, Beautifully Unfinished Woman

The characters come to life. I felt myself drawn into the journey as the Nguyen family sorted out their daughter's mental health issues and struggled to fit into American culture. I found myself clinging to the book to see how it resolved. I was there with Anh as she explored how to keep herself together through frightening changes and wanted to hold her hand through the journey. I lost myself in the story. Elizabeth Nguyen has an amazing way of sharing experiences, healing journeys and emotions in her work with vivid details and inspiring solutions to life's challenges. Her vision of crossing cultures leaves the reader wanting to learn more.

- Terri Hofstetter, Intuitive Soul Guide

In this gripping tale of two worlds, told from two perspectives, Elizabeth skillfully weaves relevant issues around mental health and coming of age, as well as cultural and generational clashes. At the heart of the story is the mother-daughter relationship told through the backdrop of the emotions of a lost culture, the grief of which can be tasted through the pages.

- Victoria Smisek, author of *Falling Awake – A Heroine's Journey*

I was captured from the word go and felt myself effortlessly flowing into the worlds of Anh as her life unfolded, fell apart and with the 'right medicine', began her healing journey. From being horrified by her initial treatments to the relief of her finding compassion from others and for herself, I felt genuine happiness as she allowed herself to follow her creativity. The descriptions of her dreams and artwork painted a vision of hope for her future. Thank you Elizabeth, your story resonated with me on a number of levels, I am sure this is going to be beautiful medicine for many.

- Brier Hart, author of *Menopause Wisdoms*

"Aloha Vietnam" tells the story of a Vietnamese American teenager who experiences a psychotic episode and is diagnosed with Bipolar Disorder. Through the perspectives of Anh and her mother Xuan, the reader learns how the illness disrupts Anh's life and how she and her mother struggle to come to terms with how their lives have changed. The novel also explores the losses that immigrants experience as well as the challenges they face while trying to bridge the gap between the cultures and traditions of their home country and those of their new country. Through a gradual acceptance of her illness and maintaining a connection to her home country, Anh discovers who she is and what brings her the most joy in life. As an Asian American child and adolescent psychiatrist, I highly recommend "Aloha Vietnam" not only for its sensitive portrayal of illness, but also for its moving depiction of an immigrant's experience.

- Dr. Harry Wang, MD, Child and Adolescent Psychiatrist

ALOHA VIETNAM

ELIZABETH NGUYEN, MD

The information given in this book should not be treated as a substitute for professional medical advice; always consult a medical practitioner. Any use of information in this book is at the reader's discretion and risk. Neither the author nor the publisher can be held responsible for any loss, claim or damage arising out of the use, or misuse, of the suggestions made, the failure to take medical advice or for any material on third party websites.

ISBN 978-1-913590-79-6 Paperback
ISBN 978-1-913590-80-2 Ebook

The Unbound Press
www.theunboundpress.com

Hey unbound one!

Welcome to this magical book brought to you by The Unbound Press.

At The Unbound Press we believe that when women write freely from the fullest expression of who they are, it can't help but activate a feeling of deep connection and transformation in others. When we come together, we become more and we're changing the world, one book at a time!

This book has been carefully crafted by both the author and publisher with the intention of inspiring you to move ever more deeply into who you truly are.

We hope that this book helps you to connect with your Unbound Self and that you feel called to pass it on to others who want to live a more fully expressed life.

With much love,
Nicola Humber

Founder of The Unbound Press
www.theunboundpress.com

This book is dedicated to the people, land, and waters of
Vietnam and Hawaii.

May love stretch across the Pacific Ocean and heal us all.

Tidelands

I.

My people arose from mountains and sea.
Joined by a marriage of dragons and spirit,
birthing life where waves caress shore.
My people hold onto the ability
to move between two worlds
in one breath.
Earth and ether,
sea and sky,
heaven and hell.

II.

I try to imagine what kept my grandparents alive
when the rice ran out.
When stomachs knot in hunger,
incense smoke clouds the air.

I try to imagine what kept my people afloat
on the boats that leaked
urine, feces, and death
into murky waters not wanting to be seen.

I try to imagine how it feels to be muted,
to have one's voice stripped away,
as I ache for my father to utter a word.

I try to imagine what is born with each of my children
as they slip out of me
toward a world
I hope will be clearer

than the one
in which I was conceived.

III.

On this side of the Pacific, the American side,
old identities fade with time,
the way pictures lose color in the sun.
I stare at a photograph of my mother
in a red áo dài dress on her wedding day.
I cannot read her face,
a face that has been lost and remade,
as easily as names are changed.

I look out towards the other side of the Pacific.
In this vast expanse of ocean,
a body large enough to contain our collective tears,
I long for the two sides to meet
so I can be whole again.

Can words stitch back two worlds?
Which way is up or down, forward or backwards?
Everything tumbles in the waves
and washes up on shore,
smooth and pleasing as sea glass.

- Elizabeth Nguyen

Prologue

Today it is impossible for me to get through school. Yesterday I was at least able to sit through my classes. I have a trick where if I repeat the same words or sentence over and over in my mind it can drown out the chattering noise and thoughts in my head. But today, despite using this technique, I can't get all the sounds and images in my head to quiet down. Words fly by so fast. Scary thoughts rush in over and over that don't make sense. Scenes from movies I have never seen flash by so rapidly that I can't slow them down. My head feels like it's going to explode from all this pressure, and I want to cover my ears and scream. I start rocking back and forth in my chair with my hands over my ears. My feet tap the floor uncontrollably. At first, no one notices, but then my classmate Kelly who is sitting next to me whispers, "Anh, are you OK?"

I don't answer because I know if I open my mouth, I won't be able to keep myself from screaming. Kelly keeps asking me, "Are you OK? Anh, are you OK?" I again shake my head back and forth and squeeze my eyes shut in a futile attempt to get the world to leave me alone. I feel a pair of hands rest on my shoulders, and a voice start calling my name, "Anh, Anh, if you can hear me, please open your eyes." As much as I don't want to open my eyes, I know that they won't leave me alone until I do. I open my eyes and see my high school English teacher Mr. McLaren kneeling down in front of me with a concerned expression on his face.

Chapter 1 - Xuan

1992

The doctor has asked me and Long to come to the hospital to have a meeting to discuss Anh. We nervously push the button to be buzzed into the unit. I am surprised by the high level of security. The locked doors make me suspicious about what they are doing to my daughter behind there. "Who are you here to see?" a voice garbles through the intercom.

"My daughter Anh is here. We have a meeting with her doctor, Dr. Tanaka," I manage to say.

The voice does not reply, but then I hear a loud buzzing noise as if the door is being electrocuted. Nothing happens. I push the button again. The same voice answers, now sounding somewhat annoyed, "You're supposed to push the door when you hear the buzzing sound. Here, try again," she states matter-of-factly as the buzzing sound starts again.

I tentatively touch the buzzing door, afraid that it might send a jolt of electricity through me if I touch it. But there is no spark of electricity, and instead, the door opens into a small waiting area, and I see that the "voice" behind the button belongs to a middle-aged haole clerk sitting behind what looks like bullet-proof glass. "You can have a seat here, and Dr. Tanaka will come and get you," she tells us, looking entirely bored by her job.

A few minutes later, a trim, professional-looking Asian lady doctor comes out of the locked doors that I presume to be where Anh is and introduces herself to me and Long.

"Hello, Mr. and Mrs. Nguyen. I'm Dr. Tanaka. Come, let's meet in the room over here," she gestures towards a locked door located off to the right of the receptionist. There are so many locked doors around here. The doctor sorts through the multiple keys that are hanging on a chain around her neck, finds the correct one, and unlocks the door to reveal a small conference room with a circular table and several chairs spaced around it. There is nothing on the walls. I have never been in an interrogation chamber before, but this room looks like it could be used for that purpose.

Long and I sit down and wait for the doctor to begin.

"Thank you for coming in today," she starts. "I'm sure you must be very concerned about your daughter, so today's meeting is an opportunity for me to share with you how Anh has been doing and answer any questions you might have about her diagnosis and treatment."

Long and I remain silent. This is all completely foreign to us. We have no idea what to expect or how to proceed.

The doctor must sense our hesitance because she starts talking again, "Why don't I start by giving you an update on Anh." She opens a file folder in front of her and flips through some pages as she talks. "When I evaluated Anh yesterday, she was very angry and irritable. The nurses told me she hasn't slept at all since arriving and was up the whole night pacing and talking to herself. She was causing a disturbance to the other adolescents on the unit, so we moved her to the isolation room where she can be more closely observed. Her urine test in the ER didn't show any evidence of drugs in her system. Has Anh ever been like this before?" she asks us.

"Of course not," Long answers defensively. "What is going on? What is happening to our daughter?" he asks.

"Well, since this is the first time Anh is presenting this way, then it's hard to be definitive with a diagnosis, but from the history thus far, it looks like Anh could be having her first manic episode," the doctor says calmly.

"What is a manic episode?" I ask, completely confused by the words the doctor has been using.

"A manic episode is when someone presents with symptoms of elevated or irritable mood, decreased sleep, rapid speech, racing thoughts, increased energy and activity, and sometimes difficulty with their thoughts."

I start to have trouble with my own thoughts. What is the doctor saying? Why can't I understand the words she is using? Long's English is better than mine so I allow him to take charge of the conversation.

"What is causing her to have this manic episode?" Long says. I notice he is repeating the same words the doctor did to show her that he is an intelligent, educated person.

"Usually, it's due to what we call bipolar disorder. Have you heard of this term, bipolar disorder, before?"

Both Long and I shake our heads.

"Let me try to explain. Bipolar disorder is an illness where someone has difficulty controlling his or her moods. Sometimes they get sad or depressed, and then sometimes they get too happy or too angry."

"Doesn't everyone get happy or sad sometimes?" Long asks.

"Yes, emotions are a normal part of our experience, but sometimes these emotions can become too severe where they cause problems in our life," the doctor continues.

I get the impression that she is trying to convince us of something.

"When do we get to take Anh home?" I ask, eager to get Anh out of this place.

"Anh is still very agitated right now. We would like to give her some medication to help calm her down," the doctor went on.

"No!" I immediately respond. I know Western medications are very "hot" and powerful, and Anh sounds like she is "too hot" right now already. The Chinese medicine doctors I went to in Vietnam taught me that a body has to be balanced between hot and cold. When your body is too hot, you feel angry and itchy and have trouble sleeping. I don't want this doctor giving my daughter any medications that will make her even more hot.

Long agrees with me on this one. "We don't want her to take medication. We want to see Anh now and take her home with us," he says politely, hopeful that the doctor will see what reasonable and trustworthy parents we both are.

"That is not possible," the doctor replies with a surprised look on her face.

"What do you mean, that is not possible?" Long asks. "We are Anh's parents, and we want to take her home now," he repeats again, this time more firmly.

"Your daughter is currently on an MH4, a 48-hour involuntary hold that can't be broken by anyone but a medical professional, and I don't think she is ready to go home yet," the doctor says, again using terms and numbers that seem purposely meant to confuse us.

"You are telling me that you can keep her here even if we don't want you to?" Long asks incredulously, as if there must be some misunderstanding about his authority as a parent.

"That's right. Your daughter is currently being held on an involuntary hold. You can't just take her home without the hospital's permission. And I don't recommend it. Anh needs treatment and medication to get better."

"So why did you ask us to come here today if you weren't going to let us take our daughter home?" I ask angrily.

"I wanted to discuss her diagnosis and treatment with you and to get your permission to give her medication."

"No medication!" I scream in panic. "What do we have to do to get her out of here?"

The doctor sighs and tries to take a different tack, "I know you're upset, and all of this information must be new and overwhelming to you, but you can't just take your daughter home. There are legal proceedings that must take place, and a judge has to decide whether she can go home or not."

I can not believe what I am hearing. These American laws make no sense to me. They talk about freedom all the time, but how can they hold my 17-year-old daughter who has done nothing wrong? Did I make a mistake raising my daughter in this country?

Long is doing a better job at controlling his response than I am. "This is very upsetting. So you are telling us that we can't take our daughter home? When can we see her then?"

"Visiting hours are from 6-7 pm."

"We will be back tonight," Long says.

"Are you sure you don't want to hear more about the medication I recommend she take? Most patients respond really well to it."

"No, we don't want to hear about your medication right now," Long answers and gets up to signal that we are done meeting. The doctor leads us out of the small meeting room, and we are "buzzed" out of the hospital unit by the floor clerk.

Long and I sit at our kitchen table. It is late, and the rest of the family has already gone to bed.

"Do you think we should ask Thầy, the Buddhist monk, to come to the hospital to see Anh?" I ask Long pensively.

"I don't think the hospital will allow it," Long answers. "Maybe we should try the medication the doctor is recommending," he says softly.

"What? How can you say that?" I ask incredulously.

"We have to trust the doctors," Long tries to reason with me.

"I don't trust them at all. Did you see that hospital they are holding Anh at? It would make anyone go crazy," I argue back, feeling like I now have to protect my daughter against the hospital and doctors and their medicines too. This has never happened to anyone in our family before. This is an American illness that American doctors made up to treat with their American medicines.

"Xuan, we are not doctors. We don't know what is wrong with Anh. We have to trust them," Long tries to convince me.

"I'm not a doctor, but she is my daughter, and I know how to take care of her better than anyone else," I yell with surprising force and anger. Long looks away, knowing that this is not the time to argue with me. I try to calm myself down. My mother taught me that when the water is boiling too hot, it is best to turn down the heat, so the water does not boil over the pot.

"I want to go to temple and talk to Thầy first about what he thinks we should do," I finally say to Long.

Thầy Son is waiting for me when I arrive at the temple. The temple is an old residential home in a quiet neighborhood in Wailupe Valley that has been converted into a Vietnamese Community Buddhist temple. The afternoon sunlight has softened, and there is a pleasant breeze coming off the green mountain valleys as I climb the wooden flight of stairs to the entrance of the temple. Mature trees create a green canopy of shade that rustles in the wind while giving off the fragrant smell of jasmine and plumeria. I slip off my sandals and enter the prayer hall, where there is a large statue of Buddha seated in the center of the room, surrounded by lights, paper lanterns, large vases filled with fresh tropical flowers, and plates stacked with fresh fruit. There is a large singing bowl off to the side that is rung during the weekend services. I light a stick of incense and kneel down to pay my respects to Buddha. I pray that my daughter Anh will be OK, that she will be healthy again. Thầy gestures for me to join him at a small table on the side of the room where there are two cups of tea.

"*Chào Thầy. Cảm ơn.* Hello, Teacher. Thank you so much for seeing me today," I say. I look at Thầy as he sits calmly in his saffron robe. His head is closely shaved in the customary style of Buddhist monks. He brings his hands together in front of his chest and lowers his head in a bow to greet me. I repeat the gesture and immediately feel a sense of calm and relief. I look into his kind eyes and know that I can trust his guidance. I will tell him about Anh and do whatever he recommends.

"Tell me, Xuan, what is bothering your heart?" Thầy asks me in a soothing voice.

I start to cry. I cannot hold back the tears from coming. "It's Anh. I don't know what's going on. Yesterday she went to school and then the police called me and Long to say that they had to take her to the hospital because she wasn't acting right. We went to see the doctor at the hospital this morning, and they won't let her go home with us. The doctor says that Anh needs medication for her to get better, but I don't trust American medication. They haven't even let us see her yet."

Thầy nods his head calmly, taking in all of my worries.

"What do you think Long and I should do?" I plead.

"I am so sorry, Xuan. This must be very scary for you. It is not your fault. It is not Anh's fault. It is no one's fault. American medicine is very different from what we are used to in Vietnam, but they are trying to help Anh. I think you need to trust the doctors and work with them to help Anh get better. Everyone at the temple will also pray for her health."

I start sobbing again, this time with both sadness and relief. Thầy has told me that it is not my fault that Anh is sick. I have felt guilty that it is my bad karma that has brought this upon Anh, that if I hadn't brought our family to America, we wouldn't be in this situation right now.

"So you think it is OK for her to take the medication?" I ask again, to make sure.

"Yes," Thầy answers firmly. "It is OK to give her the medication the doctors are recommending."

"*Cảm ơn Thầy, Cảm ơn Thầy*, thank you, thank you," I repeat as I stand up and bow my head to the ground in front of the large Buddha statue in prayer and submission.

That evening when Long and I return to the hospital to visit Anh, a different clerk greets us. She looks more friendly than the one there this morning.

"We are here to visit our daughter Anh," Long says, as calmly as if he were placing a take-out order.

The clerk passes the message along to a nurse who looks up at us and ends up ushering us into the same waiting area where we had met Dr. Tanaka that morning.

"Hello, Mr. and Mrs. Nguyen. Anh is not doing very well right now. I don't think a visit is a good idea," the nurse says.

I am about to lose my temper. I am now convinced that this hospital is somehow trying to harm Anh, and that is why they refuse to let me see my daughter.

"Dr. Tanaka promised us that we could see Anh tonight. We haven't seen her since she was admitted yesterday," Long says, with just a hint of desperation creeping into his voice as well.

"Anh is quite upset right now. She is in the isolation room because she tried to assault several members of our staff. You can see her if you'd like, but it might just make her more upset," the nurse went on.

"Of course we'd like to see her," Long replies.

"OK then, let's go," the nurse says as she motions to the clerk to buzz us all onto the unit. We step through the previously locked double doors onto the unit for the first time.

"Anh is in there," the nurse points to a white door with a glass window. There is a staff member sitting in front of the door guarding it, as if there was a danger inside. I walk up to the door that is slightly ajar and see my daughter sitting on the edge of the bed, sobbing into her hands. The room is empty and white, and she literally looks like a prisoner.

"Anh!" I cry out to her.

She lifts her head in the direction of my voice, and I see her eyes are red from crying. Tears have dried on her puffy cheeks. Her hair is uncombed, and she is wearing an ill-fitting hospital gown that is not even properly tied in the back so that I can see part of her back exposed. What are they doing to my daughter here? I break out in a sob and rush to her side.

"Ma! Get me out of here! Why are they keeping me here like this?" Anh cries to me desperately.

"*Con gái,* Daughter, Mommy and Daddy will do everything we can to get you out of here," I promise to her.

"I want to leave now!" Anh screams.

"We want to take you home too, but the doctor says we can't do that until the judge decides to let you go," I try to explain.

Anh turns on me, "Are you listening to the doctor? Whose side are you on anyway?" I have never seen her eyes so dark with anger. It frightens me.

"Of course we are on your side Anh, but this is a hospital and the doctors and judges are in charge here," I say.

Anh continues to look at me with a suspicious look. “I can’t trust anyone here. You’re all working together to keep me locked up. Get me out of here!” she screams at me.

I am shocked. I have never seen Anh behave this way before. I am convinced that the hospital must have done something to her to make her act this way. I look over to Long for some guidance. He looks just as confused and rattled as I feel.

Then Anh gets up and lunges at me. Her movement triggers the staff member sitting outside the door to quickly enter the room and grab Anh in a bear hug.

“Stop it! You’re hurting me!” Anh screams as she struggles against the hold. Several more hospital staff rush to the room. Long and I are pushed back behind the crowd, and the nurse who had initially shown us onto the unit says to us, “Visit is over. Follow me out of here.” I cannot stand to leave my daughter here in this condition. Who knows what they will do to her, but Long pushes me toward the exit.

On the drive home from the hospital, I can’t get the image of Anh screaming while being held back by several hospital staff members out of my mind. I feel completely helpless and powerless about what to do next.

“Maybe we should let the doctor give Anh the medication,” I finally say to Long. “What did the doctor call this illness that she says Anh has? Bipolar? I will do my own research about bipolar,” I say emphatically.

Chapter 2 - Anh

1992

It's my senior year of high school and I am working on a watercolor series called *Ocean* for an art show that Mrs. Rose encouraged me to enter. I love painting the ocean as a subject. When I mix my paintbrushes in the color palette, I feel like I am swimming in the swirling colors of the ocean where colors change in an infinite spectrum. My series is a collection of pieces that highlight the different shades of blue, green, and sunlight at the different beaches around the island. The bright turquoise colors of Lanikai, distinct from the intense phthalo blue palette of Waimea Bay, or the sandy limestone gray-greens of Waimanalo Bay. I work late into the night or early morning to finish a piece before going to school. I am so consumed by my painting that I haven't had time to do my homework.

I rinse my brushes in the container of water and quickly look over the syllabus for my English class before stuffing it into my backpack. Today we are scheduled to discuss *The Great Gatsby*, but I haven't read the book yet. I grab the yellow Cliffs Notes copy of the book and flip through it quickly in order to have some vague responses in case my teacher calls on me. I briefly entertain not going to school and instead spending the entire day painting and finishing up my pieces, but I know my parents will not believe me if I tell them I feel ill. My parents never allow me to miss a day of school, or even be a few minutes late unless I clearly have a fever or am vomiting. They are militaristic about my school attendance and glowed with their own pride and sense of achievement when

I brought home the Perfect Attendance award each year in elementary school.

I am tired but buzzing. I can't remember the last time I slept. I have been up for at least three nights in a row working on my paintings. My head and body feel heavy and achy. I can't sleep anyway, even if I wanted to, because my mind is racing with ideas for my art, worries about school, and plans for how I will do everything that day. I close my eyes and take a deep breath to see if that will slow my brain down, but it doesn't, and I open up my eyes so that I do not get lost in my own thoughts. As hard as I try, I can't slow down my mind to think through the simple steps I need to do to get dressed and out the door to school that day.

"Anh! Hurry up! We have to leave now!" my father yells from the garage.

"I'm coming!" I yell back, but my body feels paralyzed while my brain races in a million different directions. I have so many trains of thought going simultaneously that I don't know which one to follow so that my mind and body will synchronize.

"Come on, just put on some clothes!" my younger brother Jack yells at me from the door of my room. He is already dressed for school and doesn't like being late. He enters my messy room/art studio and picks up some semi-clean-looking items that are draped on the back of my desk chair, and throws them at me. "Here, put these on!" He has gotten used to helping me through my difficult mornings. "I already packed your lunch for you. Meet you in the car before Dad loses it."

I change out of my pajamas, throw on the shorts and t-shirt my brother picked out for me, pull a brush haphazardly through my shoulder-length hair a few times, and grab my backpack from the floor and run out to the garage where my dad already has the car running.

That day at school is more difficult than the past few days this week. Yesterday I was at least able to sit through my classes. I discovered a trick where if I repeat the same words or sentence over and over again in my mind, it would drown out the other chattering noise and thoughts in my head. But today, despite trying this technique, I can't get the sounds in my head to quiet down. My head feels like it's going to explode from all this pressure, and I want to cover my ears and scream. I start rocking back and forth in my chair with my hands over my ears. My feet are tapping the floor uncontrollably. At first, no one notices, but then my classmate Kelly who is sitting next to me whispers, "Anh, are you OK?"

I don't answer because I know if I open my mouth I won't be able to keep myself from screaming, so when Kelly keeps asking, "Are you OK?" I keep shaking my head back and forth and squeezing my eyes shut in a futile attempt to get the world to leave me alone. I feel a pair of hands rest on my shoulders and start calling my name, "Anh, Anh, if you can hear me, please open your eyes." As much as I don't want to open my eyes, I know that they won't leave me alone until I do. I open my eyes and see my English teacher Mr. McLaren kneeling down in front of me with a concerned expression on his face.

"I'm OK, Mr. McLaren, I'm OK, I just have a headache. I'll be fine. Please just leave me alone. Your voices are too loud, they're hurting my ears, please." I am vaguely aware that everyone in the classroom is turned around and looking at me.

"Anh, I think you should come outside with me," Mr. McLaren insists. I begin to get annoyed at his persistence.

"I said I'm OK. Leave me the fuck alone!" I yell at him. There is an audible gasp in the classroom. Mr. McLaren starts to squeeze my shoulders a little more firmly as if he can persuade me to cooperate, but instead, the increased pressure on my body makes me even angrier.

"Don't touch me. Get your fucking hands off of me, you pervert," I scream. I can't control what is coming out of my mouth. I don't recognize who this person is inside me screaming at my teacher, but at the same time, I know she is me. I have never dared raise my voice at a teacher in my life, much less swear at one openly.

"Kelly, would you please go to the office and let Dean Smith know that we have a situation here and need some assistance," Mr. McLaren asks my classmate.

"What situation?!?" I demand. "You're the one who won't leave me alone. Why don't you leave the *situation*?" My classmate Kelly stands paralyzed, unsure whether to follow through with the teacher's request.

"Don't just stand there with that stupid look on your face, Kelly. Go ahead, do what the teacher says, like you always do. Follow the crowd, don't think for yourself, you never do anyways," I snap at Kelly.

Kelly runs out of the classroom quickly as if she doesn't know what just hit her. The look of shock on all my classmate's faces is priceless, I bet they sure didn't expect this when they walked into English class this morning.

The rest happens in a blur. Some adults enter the classroom and escort my classmates to another classroom. There is only Mr. McLaren, the school counselor Ms. Shields, and me left in the classroom. Ms. Shields tries to use a calm and soothing voice, but every word that comes out of her mouth grates on my eardrums. Ms. Shields whispers something to Mr. McLaren about the police being on their way.

"Police?! What the fuck?! You called the frickin' police on me? What did I do wrong? I'm just here to get an education. Is it because I'm Vietnamese? Are you going to intern me like the Japs? Or are you calling the police to come and interrogate me and throw me into a reeducation camp?" The words are coming out of me from a place I didn't even know existed.

I then see two armed police officers enter the classroom. After briefly talking to Mr. McLaren and Ms. Shields, the male officer approaches me. "Hi, Anne, can you tell me what is going on here?"

"Why are you asking me? It looks like you already got all the information from those guys," I gesture in the direction of my teacher and school counselor with a nod of my head. They don't deserve the respect of being addressed by their names or titles.

"We want to hear things from your perspective," the officer continues calmly.

"Nothing is going on here. I was just sitting here in this stupid English class minding my own business when everyone keeps bugging me and won't leave me alone."

"Anne, are you using any drugs?" the officer continues.

"What?!! Are you crazy? Of course not," I answer. "This is ridiculous. Are *you* using any drugs?" I shout back at the officers.

"Anne, we want to take you to the hospital to have you checked out to see if everything is OK," the officer explains.

"I'm not going to any hospital. I need to go home and work on my paintings. There's nothing wrong with me," I insist.

"Anne, we need you to come with us," the officer says again gently, yet firmly, and as he starts to reach for my arms, something explodes inside me, and I start fighting him off with my arms as I get up and try to run toward the door. I have no idea where I need to go or what I am running from, I just need to run. The officer's arms are not gentle any longer as they grab me firmly in a bear hug. The other officer pulls my arms back behind my back to handcuff me. The last thing I remember is the overwhelming shame I feel as they drag me handcuffed out of the English building while my classmates look on in shock.

Chapter 3 - Anh

1992

I wake up in a sterile room with two twin beds and shiny tile floors that smell freshly mopped with a hospital cleaning solution. I am still wearing the clothes Jack threw to me to put on for school. But I am not at school anymore. I'm not sure where I am. I have a big headache and bruises on my forearms that I don't recall how I got. My hair is greasy and uncombed, which bothers me and makes me feel unclean.

"Good morning! You're finally awake!" a cheerful voice booms into the room. "I'm your nurse, Norma," a young Filipino lady casually dressed in a scrub top and pants introduces herself as she walks into my room with a tray of breakfast.

Nurse? I'm confused. This doesn't look like a hospital. Why do I have a nurse?

"Where am I?" I ask.

"You tell me, honey. Where do you think you are?" I can't tell if this is some weird dream or reality. And this supposed nurse's excessively sweet voice is starting to irritate me.

"I wouldn't have asked you if I knew, now would I?" I snap back, again aware of that prickly part of myself coming out from a place that feels both familiar and foreign, a mean part of me that exists alongside the nice me.

Norma does not seem fazed by my temper. "You are on the adolescent unit at Kahi Mohala Psychiatric Hospital. I brought you some food, and Dr. Tanaka will be in to see you shortly. You'll have to eat your breakfast out in the common area where we can keep an eye on you and make sure you don't hurt yourself or anyone else."

"What do you think I'm going to do? Throw an egg at you?"

"I've seen it all, baby."

Kahi Mohala? I'm at a psychiatric hospital? What the fuck happened? I don't want to step outside my room. At least from this vantage point in my bed, I can see everything and be alert to any visible threats. As I sit there in my bed, a middle-aged Japanese-looking woman with short black hair cut in a clean bob enters the room.

"Hi Anh, I'm Dr. Tanaka, the child psychiatrist on the unit," the woman speaks calmly and quietly. I am wary of strangers, but there is something soothing and non-threatening about Dr. Tanaka's voice that tells me I can let my guard down just a tiny bit, even though I have no idea what a child psychiatrist is.

"How did you sleep?" Dr. Tanaka asks.

"Like shit, my head hurts and I don't know how long I've been here."

"What do you remember?" the doctor asks. I hate how all these "professionals" ask me questions they already know the answers to, as if they are testing my intelligence.

"I don't want to answer all these questions again," I retort.

"That's understandable. You've probably been asked these same questions a million times already, and it's annoying," Dr. Tanaka replies as she sits down on the empty twin bed across from mine. Did the doctor just agree with me?

"Well, your parents and teachers were very worried about you," the doctor continues as I now vaguely remember what happened at school. Was it yesterday or earlier today or several days ago? I have no idea.

"Your parents have given permission for us to give you some medicine to help you feel better. It's a medication called Lithium, and it is a mood stabilizer to help you balance your moods...." The doctor's voice trails off as my mind starts to reel again from all this new information.

"Medication? You're drugging me? Who are you anyway?" I start suspiciously spitting out questions. I was wrong to trust this woman. It was all a part of her act to pretend to be trustworthy.

"I'm Dr. Tanaka, a child psychiatrist, a doctor who helps you with your feelings and thoughts."

"Well, I'm feeling pretty shitty right now, so you must not be doing a very good job!" I yell at her.

"The medication will take some time before you feel better. But in the meantime, you'll stay here in the hospital so I can monitor you and your response to the medication."

"I'm not staying here! I want to leave and go home right now!"

"No one likes being in the psychiatric hospital, but it's what's best for you right now."

"How do you know what's best for me? You're not me."

"You're right, I'm not you. But I want to help you." Dr. Tanaka senses that she is not going to make any further progress today and ends our conversation abruptly. "The nurse will be bringing by your medicine after you get some food in your stomach."

"I'm not taking any medication, you dumb bitch!"

"Would you like to know more about the Lithium?" Dr. Tanaka asks again calmly.

"No, I don't want to hear another word of your voice!" I yell as Dr. Tanaka stands up and walks out the door.

My senses are heightened like a hunted animal. I am sure these people are part of a conspiracy to try and hurt me. My mind races as I review possible reasons why they are holding me here. Did Punahou set me up? Are they holding me hostage so they can ask my parents for ransom money? Are my parents in on this too? Who are these other people locked up here with me? Are they also victims of this nefarious plot, or are they actors staged here to make me feel like I'm not the one being singled out? I don't know yet, so I have to be especially on guard for clues to figure this out. I quickly scan my surroundings and see that the only way into and off the unit is through the main double-locked entrance door. The rooms are located along the hallway, and there is no other way to enter and exit the unit.

"Time to line up for medication," the nurse announces to our unit after breakfast. I don't trust what they're giving out here. They're just trying to drug me up so I can be more vulnerable to their tricks. They can't force me to take medication. The doctor said something about a court hearing this morning if I refuse my medication. They probably bribe the judge to rule in their favor. I can't trust anyone. I start hearing a low male voice whispering in my ear, "Don't trust anyone. Don't trust anyone." I whip around to see who is so close to me, but when I turn around, there is no one there. I swear I heard someone's voice.

My eyes are fixed on the entrance door, scanning everyone who goes in and out, looking for an opportunity to escape, but there are always too many staff by the door. I see the doctor come onto the unit and say something to the nurse. The nurse looks up in my direction. They are talking about me, I know it. Sure enough, after the doctor goes down the hallway to talk to a patient, the nurse comes up to me. "Don't trust anyone," the voice whispers to me again. The hairs on my arm stand up. They are messing with my mind in here. The nurse is coming to tell me a lie, to get me to try and trust her, but I can't do that.

"Anne, you didn't take your Lithium this morning," the nurse says in a neutral tone. "The judge says that you have to take it or we have to give you a shot. So I'm here to offer you the medication again," she says.

I knew it, they're still trying to drug me up. "NO!! I won't take any of your medications. You can't do this to me!" I scream.

She reaches out her hand, which is holding a small paper cup with one pink capsule in it. I quickly knock the cup out of her hand and make a lunge for the entrance door, hoping that somebody might be entering the unit at exactly the same time so I can escape. But before I even make it a few steps, I feel powerful hands grab me from behind and pull my arms back like I am being handcuffed again. Someone else grabs my legs, and suddenly I am being lifted off the ground and placed face-down on a hard surface. I start screaming, "Let go of me!! Stop hurting me!!" Out of the corner of my eye, I see the same nurse who had offered me the pink pill now wearing latex gloves and holding up a syringe. As hands hold me down, I feel my pants being ripped down to expose my naked butt and then a deep stabbing pain in my right cheek as the nurse plunges the needle into me. I howl in resistance. “Don’t let them do this to you!” the voice in my head screams back.

I get in line behind a boy named Sammy and wait for my turn. The first few days at the hospital, I refused to take my medication, but that only forced them to give me a shot in the butt, so now I begrudgingly get in line to pop my pills. I try not to think too much about how ridiculous this whole setup is – locking me up, forcing me to take medication, like I’m some sort of a criminal. What did I do to deserve this? When I get to the front of the line, the nurse asks to see the name on my wristband and asks me my date of birth.

“October 3, 1975,” I reply.

She hands me a little paper cup with two bright pink pills in it. “Here’s your Lithium,” she says as she hands me another small cup of water to drink it with. I take the two pills into my mouth and wash it down with a sip of the water and then open my mouth for her to inspect that I have swallowed and not “cheeked” it. This is humiliating. I feel like a lab monkey, a helpless victim of their experiments.

I am discharged home on a Monday afternoon after the doctors returned from the weekend. They tell me I need to continue taking my Lithium 600mg tablets twice a day. The medication makes my head feel slow and uncoordinated, like I can’t complete my thoughts or move my body without a concentrated effort.

When I arrive home, I find my grandmother Bà nội praying in front of our family altar. The smell of incense drifting up into the air soothes my senses. The smell makes me feel warm and safe. Bà nội is dressed in one of her long, simple, brown Buddhist robes. She has prayer beads wrapped around both hands and is chanting, “*Nam Mô A Di Đà Phật. Nam Mô A Di Đà Phật…*” over and over again, the rhythmic sounds of the Sanskrit homage to Buddha. There is something soothing about hearing the familiar syllables being repeated over and over, washing over me like gentle lapping waves. Because the language doesn't make any sense to me, I relax even more, my mind not racing to decipher the meaning of the words. It is just sound, voice, and rhythm.

Bà nội usually prays twice a day, in the early morning and late evening, changing the water and fresh fruit on the altar and lighting incense every day to honor the ancestors and Buddha. It is unusual to find her praying in the middle of the afternoon. She is seated kneeling before the altar, her eyes closed in a deep meditative state with a concerned pleading expression on her face. When I was younger, I used to climb into Bà nội's lap or sit on the pillow next to her, just to be close to her and the smell of the incense and prayer bowl. As I got older, I joined her less frequently in front of the altar. Today, however, something calls me to sit down next to her, fold my legs underneath myself, and join her in chanting, "*Nam Mô A Di Đà Phật. Nam Mô A Di Đà Phật....*"

After her prayers, Bà nội asks if I am hungry, "*Cháu, đói không?*"

I am ravenous. The doctor says weight gain is a possible side effect of the Lithium. I can't stop eating and never feel satisfied, a growing emptiness gnawing at my core. I can feel the waistband on my pants fit uncomfortably tight around my midline. Bà nội brings to my room a bowl of *cháo gà,* chicken rice porridge, and sits down next to me and strokes my hair in rhythmic caressing gestures. As I eat, I catch sight of my unfinished paintings stacked neatly in a pile in a corner. Someone cleaned up my room while I was in the hospital. I sit up in a panic. I now remember the last time I was in my room, I had been feverishly working to finish my pieces for the student art show. Has the show already passed? How long was I in the hospital?

As hard as I try to think clearly, my mind is foggy, and it feels like I can't move boulders out of the way to get to what I want. In a panic, I grab my stack of paintings and start laying them out on the table so I can see what still needs to be done. The colors on the papers are familiar to me, but also foreign, as if they had been painted by a different person. I am not sure how to go back to finish these. I might have to start them all over again. My brain feels a surge of energy as I start to plan out how I will complete these pieces.

Bà nội looks at me with a worried expression on her face. "*Cháu ơi*, child, rest, you can paint later. You need to get your rest."

"I've already lost so much time in the hospital. I need to catch up."

"What's the rush? You're young. You need to rest to get your strength back. There will be plenty of time to paint later."

"No, you don't understand, I have to finish these paintings for the show," I try to explain. I find myself becoming frustrated when I try to get someone else to understand my point of view. Like that annoying doctor in the hospital, the one who kept me there so long. I tried to explain to Dr. Tanaka that I needed to leave the hospital so that I could finish my paintings in time for the art show, but she didn't seem to care that I needed to get back to my life. Every day she talked to me for ten minutes and told me that I needed more time to get better. I was sure that if Dr. Tanaka had her way, I would still be in the hospital. I'd heard my parents say something about the hospital telling them that I had already been there too long and that the insurance company told them it was time for me to be discharged. Dr. Tanaka arranged an appointment for me to come and see her in two weeks, but I've already made up my mind that I will never see Dr. Tanaka again.

Chapter 4 - Xuan

1979

Anh was my first child. I dreamed that her birth would mark a new chapter in our family's history, one that would hold more hope and beauty than the war-filled years of my own childhood. When I found out that I was pregnant, I knew that our family had to find a way to leave Vietnam. I wanted my children born in America, with their names and dates of birth printed on official American birth certificates, unlike my own illegitimate beginnings. I didn't even know my exact birthday. My mother said I came into her life in the Year of the Dog. My birth mother was a poor young woman who pled my mother to have mercy: "Take this girl and raise her as your own child." After suffering several miscarriages and a stillborn male child, when my mother saw my innocent face and a woman begging her to take this beautiful, healthy child home as her own to raise, she could not resist. She told me that she had wished she could have carried home a boy to my father, but a daughter to help around the house and take care of the ancestor altar was better than no child at all.

So, you see, I didn't really know the details about my beginnings in this world. Who my birth mother and blood father were, what day I was born, or the name I was given. I can proudly say that my daughter Anh Lien Nguyen was born in Honolulu, Hawaii, on October 3, 1975, in the Year of the Rabbit. My husband Long and I left Vietnam in April 1975 with Long's family. Long's older sister Thuy had married an American military officer named Thomas, and they were already living in America, in Honolulu, Hawaii, where Thomas was stationed. At a time when leaving the country was a mess, we were grateful that Thuy and Thomas helped make arrangements for our family's safe departure from Vietnam.

Long and I had been college classmates, and our parents had agreed to our marriage. Long's father died of illness when he was young, and since he was the oldest son, his mother looked to him to make decisions for their family. I did not realize at the time how the decision to stay in Vietnam or leave for America would so dramatically alter our family's path. It all happened so quickly; we only had days to pack up, sell our belongings to have some cash on hand, and leave before the Communists arrived in Saigon. I was sad to leave my country, the place of my birth, but I had no time to mourn or even think about what was happening. I had to focus on preparing to leave, not sure when I would, or could, come back. I tried to convince my own parents to come with me to America. I could not bear the thought of leaving them behind, but my father refused to move again. He had already relocated from Hanoi to Saigon in 1954 after the country was divided by leaders in Geneva, and he refused to uproot himself again because of the whims of politicians who signed papers dictating the lives of millions of powerless people.

"Xuan, my daughter," Father stubbornly argued, "The Vietnamese people have been pushed around like dust. If this is the only decision I get to make in my life, then I choose to stay." My mother also did not want to leave the land where her parents and ancestors rested.

"If I come with you to America now, who knows one day they won't decide to send us back?" my father reasoned. "This is my country and I am going to die here. I don't want to die in some place where people can't even pronounce my name." As I hastily prepared our bags for departure, I felt the very fiber of my identity being torn apart. I promised my parents I would come back to visit and prayed that perhaps they would come to visit me one day too, but we all knew that these were empty words to soften the pain of separation. We did not know when, or if, we would ever see each other again.

The day we boarded the plane to leave Vietnam, there were five of us – Long, his mother, his two younger brothers, and me. I was young, newly wed, pregnant, and terrified. We were surrounded by others also on their way to America. Many families were headed to California, or Texas, or other unfamiliar-sounding states, but I could not find another family headed to Honolulu as their final destination and not just a layover. "Thuy says the weather in Hawaii is similar to Vietnam," Long told his mother. "It will be easy for you to adjust there," he reassured her, as if warm tropical weather alone could ease the transition to a foreign land.

Within minutes of landing in Honolulu, Long's sister Thuy wasted no time in telling us, "You must find jobs, first thing. The government will not support you very long." This news smacked me in the face like the monsoon winds of home. We had been so preoccupied with just leaving and getting here that I had thought little about what we'd do once we arrived.

"But where will we look for work?" I asked in the back seat of Thomas's car as we drove back to their apartment.

"There is a small network of Vietnamese refugees here in Honolulu who will help you find work. But since you don't speak English well, you will not be able to teach school as you did in Saigon," Thuy told me.

Within a week, I found myself slicing pineapples at the Dole cannery. But on the third morning at the Cannery, one of my co-workers shouted, "Xuan, look at your hands and arms!" My forearms were covered with red blotches that by the end of the shift were itchy and swollen. I found out I was allergic to pineapple juice and could not return to work at the cannery.

Thuy told me, "I found a job for you doing nails." I was nervous about this. I had never been particularly good at working with my hands – the needlework I did to hem and patch our family's clothes was an embarrassing display of my inept handiwork. My first day at Lucky Nails, my boss Hai, an older Vietnamese man, instructed a veteran employee Ngoc to train me.

"Ask your customers, 'How are you today?'" Ngoc told me as she demonstrated how to operate the soaking tub. "If you don't understand what they say to you, just smile and nod and tell them how pretty they look. You must learn those two lines – 'How are you?' and 'You look very pretty today.'" I practiced these two lines to myself, struggling to let the strange words slip through my lips as awkwardly as if there is a rubber band tied around my tongue. But Ngoc was right. These two lines served me well in many situations in Hawaii besides the nail salon. I repeated these words to the bus driver, the lady at the grocery store, and the bank teller, and was always met with smiles and nods of approval. I was surprised at how easily Americans were swayed by the power of words, especially flattering ones, as if they don't care whether the words were true or not, but simply that they were uttered. My parents taught me to not trust words alone. "Talk is cheap, it is one's actions that truly define one's character," my father said. "Be careful of those who talk too much, they're probably trying to hide something," my mother told me. As a dutiful daughter, I tried my best to listen more than speak, but I am not sure if my parents' advice in Vietnam would serve me as well here in America. I noticed that when I did not speak here in this new land, everyone seemed to forget I was even here.

My husband Long was an engineer in Vietnam, but in Honolulu he found work as a parking lot attendant in Chinatown. Long was never one to complain. His "office" was a small enclosure the size of a telephone booth with a small rotating desk fan to keep him cool from the intense humid climate, but he told me, "At least it is in the shade."

I had a devoted following of customers at the nail salon who praised my gentle touch and attention to detail, but I was not satisfied with my boss reaping all the financial rewards of my labor. No matter how hard I worked, I had to depend on the generosity of tips to save any money. I dreamed about having my own business and being my own boss.

"Be patient, Xuan. We knew this was not going to be easy," Long always told me when I became restless and frustrated. Our family got our first lucky break in Hawaii when I found our store. I was riding the bus home from the nail salon in Waikiki to our apartment in Salt Lake when I noticed a sign in front of a small storefront along the shops between the Ilikai hotel and the Japanese hibachi steak house that read

"Business For Sale." I believed in signs from the universe, and goosebumps ran down my arms when I saw this sign. Even though I had just gotten on the bus, I pulled the plastic cord that ran the length of the bus to request a stop. I hopped off the bus and headed directly to the storefront with the "For Sale" sign. A thin, middle-aged Asian lady with brittle black hair that looked like it had been colored and permed too many times was standing near the shop entrance, folding t-shirts on a table. In Hawaii, everyone was curious to know a person's particular Asian ethnicity, and I tried to guess what Asian ethnicity this lady was – maybe Korean? Hardly anyone ever guessed that I was Vietnamese, unless they saw me in the nail salon. There were only a small number of Vietnamese people living here in Hawaii in the years after 1975, and we were greatly outnumbered by other Asian groups like the Japanese and Chinese.

"Can I help you?" the store owner asked me in her heavily accented English, revealing her Chinese origin. Different Asian groups preferred dealing with their own kind, especially in matters of business, but when that was not possible, we put aside our differences in the common cultural interest of making money for all.

"I saw your sign – 'Business For Sale,'" I told her.

She looked at me and studied me closely from top to bottom as if she was internally calculating if I was someone who had enough money to make this conversation worthwhile.

"I am selling my store," the woman finally answered as she gestured her hand toward the small space behind her. The store was shaped like a long narrow shoebox. The walls were lined with glass shelves that held folded t-shirts emblazoned with designs of rainbows, hula girls, and "Hawaii '79." Underneath the shelves were piles of beach-friendly footwear, beach mats, and towels. The center of the store had several circular racks with hanging aloha shirts and muumuus, and at the front of the store was a rotating postcard stand with colorful cards depicting various scenic points around the islands.

"How much?" I found myself asking.

"The rent is $1000 a month, and you can buy all the merchandise I have to get started for $5000." I hid my reaction, knowing that I did not have anywhere close to that much money. The rent alone was more than our family paid for the small two-bedroom apartment that we shared with Long's sister Thuy.

"Why are you selling the business?" I asked, trying to gather more information.

"I am moving to a bigger store on Kalakaua Avenue. I've been here 10 years, business is good, right next to the Hilton Hawaiian Village," the lady continued. I suspected she was not telling me the entire truth, because she would not be selling the business if it was good, but I was used to making decisions based on partial truths.

"Let me talk to my husband and I will come back," I told her as I walked out to the bus stop to wait for the next bus.

I was nervous about approaching Long with my idea. Long was a conservative man who didn't like taking risks. I summoned up the courage to bring it up anyway, "Long, I want to talk to you about something."

Long raised his eyebrow. He knew that whenever I started a conversation this way, it was going to be serious.

"Go ahead," he said warily.

"I was riding the bus home from work today through Waikiki, and I saw a shop for sale. I want to open our own business." There, I had said it.

Long had lots of reservations. "What kind of shop is it?" he asked.

"It's a tourist shop, like the ones that sell aloha shirts and muumuus," I answered.

"An aloha-wear store? There's so many of them. What makes you think we can be successful? Why is the business for sale anyway? Probably too much competition," Long responded with all of his concerns at once.

"There's so many of them because there are many tourists. We can work hard and be better than the others. If we want to have our own place and send our children to good schools, we have to make more money than we do now," I pleaded, knowing that linking this business venture with our future children's educations would help convince him. Long and I had agreed that we wanted our children to have the best education we could find. Education was the only way to ensure success in America. We didn't want our children to have to struggle for money like we did. Money was the currency to success in the world, and those who didn't have enough of it would struggle their entire lives. I didn't leave Vietnam to have our family and children struggle forever.

"How much does the business cost?" Long asked, now curious about the actual details.

"$5000 to buy the business and merchandise. Rent is $1000 a month," I replied, knowing these were big figures.

"$5000?!? How can we even afford that?" Long asked incredulously. "Are you crazy?! We only have $300 in the bank!"

I had thought this through and presented my plan. "I will go ask Cô Thanh for a loan, and we will pay her back once the store starts making money." Cô Thanh was a successful Vietnamese businesswoman in Hawaii who owned a chain of phó restaurants. She was known as the go-to person in the Vietnamese community if you needed a loan. She charged exorbitant interest fees, but there was no other option for refugees with no credit.

"I don't know about this...what if it doesn't work, we could lose everything," Long replied.

"What can you lose when you have so little to begin with already?" I countered.

"I'm tired of risking so much," Long sighed.

"The Americans say, 'No pain, no gain.' If we don't take this risk, we'll be working hard all of our lives in minimum-wage jobs and not getting anywhere. Do you think I enjoy scrubbing people's feet and painting their nails every day for a few dollars tip?"

Long could not argue with this point. I knew he also felt ashamed of his job as a parking lot attendant. "Maybe I can pick up a second job at night so we can still have two paychecks while you start the shop," Long thought out loud.

"You would do that?" I responded, surprised, expecting him to put up more of a fight.

"I would do that for our family," Long replied.

I felt a knot of emotion swell up in my throat. Like most Vietnamese husbands, Long was not an affectionate man, but this was one of those times where I felt a surge of love for him, and I reached out to hug him. He returned my embrace with an awkward pat on my back. Before going to bed that night, I lit incense on our family altar and prayed to Buddha to support our family with this next endeavor.

Long and I started monitoring foot traffic daily around the store, parking our car across the street and observing how many customers walked into the store, and how many walked out with a purchase in hand. The shop was located on a side street of Waikiki and did not get as much foot traffic as a store that was located directly on Kalakaua or Kuhio Avenue would, but there were enough tourists to go around in Waikiki. We observed a steady stream of multi-generational Japanese families, young and old honeymooners, and families with young children walking out with shopping bags in hand.

After a week of this surveillance and calculating that there were enough customers to make a profit, I returned to the shop where I saw the "Business For Sale" sign. I found the middle-aged Asian owner rearranging a pile of plastic beach sandals. It had been ingrained in me and my fellow Vietnamese people, and perhaps in all of the developing world, to never pay full price for anything, so I was prepared with a counteroffer.

"I buy your store merchandise for $2000," I offered the shop owner.

"$4000," the owner replied without hesitation. I was excited that the price was now open to negotiation.

"$3000," I replied.

"$3500," the owner shot back.

"OK, $3500," I agreed. I could have kept going, but I did not enjoy haggling over money, and Long and I had agreed the night before that we would pay up to $3500. I dreamt of a day when I could afford to buy something without haggling about the price tag. For now, every dollar in our family budget was carefully calculated, and every purchase accounted for. I knew that a twenty-pound bag of rice would last our household two months, two gallons of milk would last one week, and a box of laundry detergent would last three months, and that the paychecks that Long and I brought home would cover our expenses for the next month.

I pulled out an envelope from my purse and counted out thirty-five crisp $100 dollar bills in front of the shopkeeper. I placed the stack of bills back in the unsealed envelope and handed it over to her. The woman went behind the glass counter to grab a plastic diamond-shaped keychain decorated with a golden sunset and black-silhouetted palm trees. The ring had three keys on it – "This one is for the front door, this one is for the side door, and this one is for the bathroom outside and to the back. Good luck." I opened up my hands to receive the keychain. I wrapped my fingers tightly around the three metal keys, afraid that if I held them too loosely, I might look down and realize there was nothing there after all.

Chapter 5 - Anh

1982

Jack and I often played hide and seek at our parents' store. I heard my younger brother Jack counting, "...seven, eight, nine, ten, ready or not, here I come!" I hurriedly pushed back the circular row of muumuus and climbed into the center of the rack, and pulled back the curtain of clothes around me. The long muumuu racks were my favorite place to hide. I liked pressing my face into the brightly colored floral patterns, breathing in the new smell of the fabrics, and feeling the crisp unworn material brush against my skin. The only problem with hiding here was that my brother always found me immediately. "Found you!" he exclaimed as he pulled back the bright-colored dresses, and called out, "My turn to hide!" I put my hands over my eyes and started counting out loud, "One, two, three, four...." Jack and I found a million different ways to entertain ourselves at our parents' store during the summer. I helped my mom fold t-shirts, roll up beach mats, and put misplaced postcards back into their proper spot. When we got tired, we went to the back of the store, where my mom created a cozy corner of beach towels and blankets underneath a rack of aloha shirts for us to take a nap. Sometimes a tourist would be browsing through the rack of aloha shirts and unexpectedly find me and my brother lying underneath.

There were always people coming in and out of the store – customers, visitors, and deliveries. One of my favorite people was Mr. Lee, who delivered aloha shirts with his assistant Kang to my parents' store every week. "Hello!" Mr. Lee hollered as he entered the store with a pile of aloha shirts piled high on his shoulder, obstructing his face. He and his assistant looked like two strange headless creatures walking with bundles of clothing piled on their shoulders. The shirts were tied together in bundles of twelve with strips of cloth scraps that I collected and fashioned around my waist like a belt. I had a growing collection of colorful cloth belts that I was very proud of. It was fun looking at them and choosing which colorful print of flowers and palm trees to tie around my waist for the day. After Mr. Lee put down his load of aloha shirts, he reached into his pockets and grabbed several pieces of Japanese rabbit candy that he always slipped to me and Jack.

"How's business today?" he asked my mom in his Korean accent.

"Not too bad. I need some more small sizes of these muumuus. The Japanese tourists like them and they are very small. I don't need the large and XL sizes, the haole tourists don't buy them, they say they are too expensive," my mother replied. "Take them back," she said, grabbing the larger sized muumuus off the rack and handing them to him, "Exchange them for small and medium-sized ones for me."

"Anything you want, Mrs. Xuan," Mr. Lee answered her jovially with a mischievous smile. We'll be back tomorrow. Bye-bye, kids!" Mr. Lee called out as he and his assistant jumped back into their white delivery truck to make their next delivery in Waikiki.

"Mommy, what does a tourist mean?" I asked her.

"It means someone who's on vacation. Lots of people come to Hawaii for vacation," she explained.

"Are we tourists?" I asked.

She laughed at my question. "No, we are refugees, not tourists."

"What is a refugee?" I asked.

"Too hard to explain. I'll tell you when you are older," she said. "Now go fold these towels," she said, as always, sending me away to a task when she wanted to end the conversation.

It was the first day of second grade, and my mom made me wear a magenta-pink jumpsuit that scratched uncomfortably at my neck. My hair was pulled back with clips that were too tight on my head. My parents made such a big deal about taking me to the first day of school. My dad put on the only suit he owned, and my mom always got her hair permed for the event. As we drove up to the school parking lot, I felt immediately embarrassed at how my parents looked. Other kids' parents were just wearing regular clothes, like shorts and t-shirts, while mine looked like they were going to a fancy party. My parents and I walked to my classroom. "Good morning, Mrs. Higuchi," my father greeted my teacher with a formal handshake and bow. I found my seat that had my name written across the top of the desk. My dad pulled out his camera, "Anh, look over here, smile!" and snapped pictures of me sitting at my desk. Then my mom squeezed in next to me, "Long, take a picture of the two of us." My dad then motioned to Mrs. Higuchi to join us, "Please, take a picture with Anh too." My cheeks got flushed and red at how much fuss my parents were making, I was relieved when the bell finally rang, signaling them to leave. "Bye, Anh! Listen to your teacher and study hard!" my mom called as my dad snapped a few more pictures on their way out.

I sat back in my chair and quietly looked around the classroom. The room was brightly lit, and the rectangular desks were arranged in groups of four, with the corners of the four desks pushed together to make an even larger rectangle. Sitting next to me was a boy with curly blonde hair named Kirk. I didn't recognize him from last year, so he must have been new this year. Across from him was a Japanese boy named Kevin, and sitting directly in front of me was a skinny girl with straight light-brown hair named Karen. She had a different teacher from me last year, so I didn't know her very well. I noticed that everyone's name started with a K except for mine. Mrs. Higuchi asked us to take out our notebooks and share what we did this past summer. Other kids talked about visiting their families, or going to Disneyland, or traveling to places I had never heard of. No one else talked about spending their summer at their parents' store in Waikiki.

At lunchtime, I opened my lunch box and took out the two thermoses that Bà nội packed me – a hot thermos of steamed white rice alongside a separate thermos of braised-tomato tofu. My lunch didn't look like other kids' lunches in my class. Instead of cute purple containers filled with ham and cheese sandwiches sliced down the middle into triangles, cups of baby carrots, and sticks of string cheese, my lunch looked like a family-style Chinese dinner. I wanted to hide my food under the table and eat it as quickly as I could so one could see how different it was from everyone else's.

Chapter 6 - Xuan

1982

Our business grew quickly. Hawaii was a particularly popular destination for Japanese tourists, so I learned a few Japanese phrases the same way I learned my first English phrases, "How are you? You look so pretty," at the nail salon. I now repeated these phrases to Japanese customers as they browsed aloha shirts and muumuus, "Kawaii! Yasui desu." It's so cute! And cheap. Being successful in Hawaii required the skills of a cultural chameleon, adapting to whatever landscape presented itself, blending in, surviving, and moving forward.

After a few years of owning the shop, Long and I saved up enough money to move out of our shared apartment with his sister Thuy into our own rental in the same apartment complex. We began to save money to buy our own place in Hawaii. Living on an island, owning a piece of land to call your own, no matter how small, was the ultimate prize.

I prided myself on providing good customer service. Our store (which we named LX Fashions for our names, Long and Xuan) was open 7 days a week from 8 in the morning to midnight. There were always tourists up at all hours of the day who were in urgent need of a beach towel, an aloha shirt to wear to a luau, or a gift to take home before they left for the airport. I approached each customer's request as a matter of the highest importance. "You need to find a t-shirt for your three-year-old grandson? Ok, I found it. You need matching aloha shirt and muumuu set for luau dinner tonight? OK, I get it for you." I was proud that Long and I were doing everything we could to assure our children a successful future.

The air conditioning in our store was not working this afternoon. I switched on the two rotating fans and set them at full speed. The hot air moved back and forth across my sweaty body and provided some relief, but not much. My eyelids got heavy, and I was about to nod off into sleep when a well-dressed Caucasian man in a suit walked into the store. His well-tailored navy-blue suit with a pink tie immediately distinguished him from the usual customer.

"Do you sell any sunglasses?" he asked me. "My friend's getting married, and it's so bright out there." He looked intelligent and had a friendly face and smile. Vietnamese people believed that we could determine someone's personal characteristics just by studying their facial features. Kind and gentle faces marked someone trustworthy. Big foreheads foretold intelligence. Slanted eyes or high cheekbones indicated potential arrogance. Here in America, whenever someone impressed me with the appearance of success, I interrogated them for information on how to garner that prosperity for my own children and family.

"Where are you from?" I asked the man directly.

"I was born here, but I live on the mainland now. I'm back home on business."

"What do you do?"

"I'm a real estate developer."

"Where did you go to school?" I always asked people where they went to school so I could find the best school for Anh and Jack, who were then in elementary school.

"I went to Punahou for high school and then to UC Berkeley for college," he answered. Punahou, I kept hearing that name. I was worried about how America was influencing my children. I had recently noticed with distaste how frequently Jack and Anh complained about everything, how hot their food was, how bored they were at the store, how they didn't have fun toys, and so on. They were becoming spoiled. Children in Vietnam did not complain. If they did, they would likely be rewarded with a sound beating. But here in America, we parents were told that children could not be physically disciplined, or else Child Protective Services would be called. I did not understand why the American government cared so much about how families disciplined their children. Didn't they have bigger concerns to worry about?

I later mentioned to Long, "I keep hearing about this school named Punahou. We need to send our kids to school there." Long had heard nothing about this place named Punahou but acknowledged that my instincts and decisions in this new country had all been good for our family. "OK," he agreed.

Chapter 7 - Anh

1985

Kumu Kealoha visited our fourth-grade classroom every week for Hawaiiana class. Kumu always wore a long, colorful muumuu and tucked a vibrant hibiscus or plumeria flower amongst her silvery gray hair behind her ear. In our Hawaiiana class, I learned how to make kukui nut leis, shining the nuts with their own oils to bring out their gleam before stranding them together into a bracelet or lei. Kumu taught us how to count from one to five in the native Hawaiian language, "*Ekahi, elua, ekolu, eha, elima!*" I listened closely to the stories she told our class about brave warriors, powerful medicine women, and mischievous children or *keiki* who played in the ocean all day. "The naupaka flower is a flower found in the mountains or near the beach. It looks like only half a flower with half of its petals missing, and legends say it is a Hawaiian princess called Naupaka who was separated from her lover, a fisherman named Kaui. Because the two lovers could not be together, they separated. One lived down by the sea, while the other lived up in the mountains, and these two half-flowers represented their torn love." I was fascinated by these beautiful colorful stories. Kumu ended her lessons with a song on her ukulele and sometimes even a hula dance. I loved my school, my teachers, and my friends.

"Anh, you are going to go to Punahou for school next year," my mom told me when I got to the store after school.

"What?! Why do I have to change schools?" I asked my mom.

"Because Punahou is a very good school. You will be successful if you go there," she answered.

"But I don't want to change schools and leave all my friends," I cried, feeling a sinking feeling in my heart. Was my mom being serious? How could she make me change something so important in my life?

"You talk too much. I didn't ask you what you wanted. When you get older, you will understand. For now, you will do what your daddy and I tell you," she said, ending the conversation.

I didn't think my parents understood how I had finally started to feel like I fit in at my school. Now I had to start all over again?

I was always nervous on the first day of school, but especially my first day at a new school like Punahou, where I didn't know anyone. I remember my first day of kindergarten when I also didn't know anyone. But no one knew each other in kindergarten when everyone was starting out together. In fifth grade, everyone already had their friends, and I'd be the new kid. My palms were clammy, and my stomach was rumbling uncomfortably. My parents sitting in the front seat of the car did not seem to notice. "You are a lucky girl to get to go to this school Punahou. It is an expensive school, so you must study hard and make the most of it," my mom said to me as they dropped me off at the curb. Lately, business was slow at the store, and my parents were stressed about money. I heard them arguing at night about money and business. I didn't want to be ungrateful for the money they were spending to send me to this private school.

I watched my parents drive away, leaving me alone to figure out where to go and how to get through my first school day. Groups of kids were walking together to their classrooms, their shared laughter carrying through the air. I checked my orientation sheet and saw that my classroom was located in Castle Hall and that my assigned teacher's name was Mrs. Yamaguchi. I looked at the campus map in the school planner and traced a route to the building labeled Castle Hall. Castle Hall was a large whitewashed three-storied building lined with large windows that opened up and out towards the roof. I stared up at the intimidating building and climbed the large stone steps to get to the entrance. I walked in and found a receptionist seated behind a desk. She looked at me over the rim of her eyeglasses. "Can you tell me which classroom is Mrs. Yamaguchi's?" I asked.

"It's on the third floor in room 18," she replied.

"Thank you," I answered and started to make my way to the central staircase located in the middle of the lobby.

"No, no, you need to go up the side stairwells located at the end of each hallway. Only teachers and staff go up the center," the receptionist scolded me. I immediately froze in fear of breaking a rule, and my face blushed hot red with embarrassment.

The receptionist noticed my response and immediately softened her voice, "Don't worry, you're not in trouble. It's the first day, your teacher will explain how everything works," but I was already hurrying down the hallway. I climbed two flights of stairs to the third floor and walked down the hallway looking for room 18. It turned out to be the third classroom on the right side of the hallway. It was a bright classroom with natural light streaming in from the large windows. A green chalkboard ran the length of the front wall of the classroom and there were five rows of five desks each facing the chalkboard. The smell of chalk was comforting to me. A seating chart hung near the doorway with student's names written on their assigned desks. I found my name and went to sit down in the second to last row. I was one of the first students in the classroom, and I sat nervously as I watched other students come in and find their seats. Mrs. Yamaguchi was an old, thin Japanese woman who sat behind her desk in the front corner of the room. She was looking through some papers and did not seem to pay any attention to the bustling of students around her.

When the 8 am bell rang marking the beginning of class, Mrs. Yamaguchi stood up from behind her desk and walked briskly to the front of the classroom. "I'm going to call roll now to see who is here. Raise your hand when I get to your name," she said as she began reciting the names on the classroom roster in alphabetical order. "Hirota, Jackson, Kitagawa, Lum, Morris." There was an inevitable pause when she got to my name. "Na-goo-yen?" she tried.

I was prepared – it always happened, and I had learned that it was best to present the bastardized version of my name rather than try to explain the silent *ng* sound and tonal sing-song rhythm that marked the correct Vietnamese pronunciation of my surname Nguyen.

"That's me, Anne New-yen," I piped up and presented the Americanized version of my first name as I divided my surname into two easy-to-pronounce English syllables, making it easier to pronounce, even if it wasn't correct. This was a skill that I had already learned at school – don't draw too much attention to myself, and try to make others feel comfortable with my different-ness. I had gotten so used to introducing myself as "Anne New-yen" that I was embarrassed to admit that, at times, I felt more comfortable with the incorrect pronunciation of my name rather than the authentic Vietnamese pronunciation. I wanted to fit in and be like everyone else, without quite knowing exactly how to do that. I didn't want to ask for help, not that I would even know what to ask for, so I constantly pretended to know what everyone else already seemed to know.

When I was younger, I didn't know what it meant to be Vietnamese. I only sensed that my family was somehow different from all the other local families I knew. But aren't all families different? Who knew what other families were like except for the people in those families? There were a lot of Asians in Hawaii, so I looked like I could be a fourth-generation local Japanese or Chinese girl whose grandparents had come to Hawaii 100 years ago to work on the sugar cane plantations. But I wasn't. My family had only been in Hawaii a little longer than I had. They had no idea what being American was, much less Hawaiian, or local. They were just winging it, and I was along for the ride. Like seabirds that flew over the ocean, dropping seeds that found their way to random shores, my brother Jack and I were born on the island of Oahu in the middle of the Pacific Ocean, thousands of miles from where our parents and grandparents were born. And as hard as we tried, it seemed like there would always be a gulf between where we came from and where we were.

On Sunday, my mom and Bà nội took me and Jack to go grocery shopping in Chinatown. Shopping in Chinatown was a hot, tiring, and smelly business. We parked in a dark, tiny parking lot that always stunk like dried urine. The streets in Chinatown were dirty, and the food stalls, especially the ones selling fresh fish and meat, gave off the odor of blood mixed with brine. I carefully navigated my steps around puddles of dirty water and food spills to avoid getting my feet soiled. My mom led us through a maze of shops and stalls, picking up different items from each one. Miniature apple bananas and mangoes from the corner stand, *lạp xưởng* Chinese sausage, *chả lụa* Vietnamese pork loaf, rice, and *nước mắm* fish sauce from the woman three stalls down, French bread from the sandwich shop, and fresh fish, meat and vegetables from the large grocery store across the street. Each stop we made left us with more heavy plastic bags that we had to carry all the way back to our car. I wished my family shopped at the American grocery stores like my friends did, where there was air conditioning and carts to pile your food into, and the aisles were clean and organized with words and labels I could read.

Our last stop in Chinatown was always to visit the Chinese medicine man between the jewelry store and the bakery shop. With our hands full of plastic bags filled with meat and produce, Bà nội led me into the herbalists' store, where the scent of musty roots and menthol-based rubbing oils filled the air. The entire wall from floor to ceiling was stacked with rows of drawers with metal handles. Each drawer was labeled with strange Chinese characters.

"*Thưa Thầy*, medicine doctor, please examine my grandchildren and let me know which herbs they need to help them be strong and healthy," Bà nội asked the store owner.

"Come here, little girl, you are getting tall." The herbal doctor said the same thing to me every week when he motioned me to the back of his shop, where there was a small card table with two metal folding chairs facing each other. He sat down on one side and waved for me to take the seat across from him. He had a large brown mole on the upper right side of his lip that had a very long hair growing from it. I couldn't help myself from staring at his long-haired mole every time I saw him and wanted to say, "Your mole hair is getting very long" every time he told me how tall I was getting.

He lay my wrist down on a small red pillow to take my pulse. He asked me to open my mouth and stick out my tongue. He examined my tongue with a curious expression and scribbled strange characters onto a piece of paper that he handed to his wife. My exam was over, and it was now Jack's turn to be examined by the medicine man.

The Chinese medicine man's wife read his scribbled handwriting and tore off a large square of thick pink butcher paper to lay down on the countertop. Methodically she went through her husband's list of ingredients and pulled down drawers one by one to fill his prescription. From one drawer, she retrieved a light-colored bark that resembled dried cuttlefish, in another were round brown seeds that looked like peppercorns, and in still another, she pulled out what looked like handfuls of shiny black seaweed. After the medicine man's wife piled seven or eight ingredients onto the large square of pink paper, she folded up the sides into a large envelope and tucked the last corner into the opening formed by the other three corners. She tied the package with twine and handed it to my grandmother. She did the same for my brother's prescription. The packages looked pretty, but my brother and I knew how awful these herbs tasted after my grandmother brewed them at home. The bitter-smelling and even worse-tasting concoction that my grandmother made me and my brother drink each day made me sick to my stomach.

Chapter 8 - Anh

1987

At the ocean, I forgot all about my family being different. I forgot about everything except the water. My parents never took a day off from work. Besides, they didn't like being out in the sun and were afraid of the ocean, so I depended on the good graces of my friends' parents to give me rides to the beach. My friend Kristy lived close by, and her dad was always willing to drive us to the beach. Today we were going boogie boarding at Waimanalo Beach. The waves at Waimanalo were perfect for boogie boarding. Even though they looked large and rumbling, once you got into the water, you realized that these waves were benign teddy bears with no bite. They wrapped you up in their large arms, but the most they would do was tussle your hair and send you for a little tumble through the gentle cycle. These Waimanalo waves wouldn't hurt you, which was reassuring for a novice Vietnamese-American twelve-year-old girl whose parents didn't approve of her going to the beach.

I had to be careful about telling my parents where I was going whenever I went out. This morning I asked my mom, "Can I go over to my friend Kristy's house?" I didn't offer any information about where we were going, or what we are planning to do. My mom didn't ask too many specific questions anyway. If she did, I answered something generic like, "We might go to Kahala Mall." It wasn't a complete lie. We might do that, it was always a possibility. My parents considered Ala Moana or Kahala Mall as "safer" places to hang out than the beach. They thought the likelihood of me getting physically injured at the mall was significantly less than in the wilds of nature.

Kristy's dad picked me up in his beat-up red Subaru station wagon and had packed an extra boogie board for me. I wore my bathing suit under my t-shirt and jean shorts and stuffed a beach towel and a pair of underwear to change into in the bottom of my backpack. As we headed past Hanauma Bay towards Waimanalo Beach, Kristy asked me, "Don't your parents ever suspect that you're going to the beach?"

"I don't know, maybe, but as long as they don't find out, it doesn't matter," I replied.

Kristy's dad gave me a disapproving look in the rear-view mirror as we turned into the street right after the Waimanalo Marketplace and McDonald's. We parked our car on the side of the road next to a narrow sandy beach access path. I loved these hidden walkways that looked like nothing from the side of the road but were a path to paradise for those who knew where to access them.

Instead of palm trees, Waimanalo Beach was shaded by a grove of ironwood trees whose thin pine needles made a soft blanket of ground cover punctuated by small, peanut-sized, poky pinecones. The powdery white sand was blindingly bright underneath the midmorning sun, and the water was a beautiful turquoise blue that mainlanders could not believe was real. The color of the Pacific Ocean was even more beautiful in real life than it looked in touched-up magazine spreads. The stretch of sand was wide and expansive, so even on a busy weekend day, it never felt crowded.

We grabbed our boogie boards out of the trunk, picked a spot under some shade to throw down our bags and beach mats, and ran toward the water. The ocean rushed up to wrap around my feet and ankles like a warm embrace between reunited friends. The strength and power of the ocean surprised me every time, splashing my body, and getting me more wet than I was ready for. It was a force like no other. I entered the ocean, letting my body become one with the water, letting its larger body wash away anything I was carrying, any thoughts, worries, or stresses I was holding. I jumped in and dived completely underwater, submerging myself like a dolphin or sea turtle. I studied the movement of the water, the direction of the wind and the current, mentally making a note of how far down the shore I was from the lifeguard stand as a landmark to reorient me if the wind blew me down shore. A wave broke in front of me, sending forth white foam directly at me. I jumped up with my boogie board to hurdle over the wave. Another wave was already curling up behind.

Today was a good-sized day. The waves weren't too big and choppy, but still big enough for a fun ride. After jumping over several waves, I finally reached a spot past the whitewash where the water was calmer. I floated in the lull between waves to wait for one that was just the right size and shape. Knowing when and where a wave will break, and where to position oneself to best increase the probability of catching that wave was a practice that couldn't be taught in a book or instruction manual, but rather through repeated trial and error, practice, and a dose of luck. I knew the basics about kicking and paddling as fast as I could when I saw the water start rising, but catching a wave was like asking the ocean for a dance – she always ultimately had the choice to refuse you. I saw a wave forming and turned around and paddled as fast as I could, but couldn't seem to get quite enough speed to catch it as it rolled by and through. The next wave was already forming, and I again paddled into position. This time I kicked and kicked and stroked harder and harder until I felt the familiar lift of the wave pick me up. Yes! I caught it! I dropped into the wave, that special place where the wave held me like a mother cradling her baby. I was off! My board was riding on the energy and speed of the wave, and all I had to do now was hold on for the ride. And what a fun ride it was. I could spend hours in the water, catching wave after wave, delighting in the sheer joy of playing with the ocean, a playmate who never fatigued. *Will you keep playing?* the ocean and I asked each other back and forth, and the answer was always yes. At some point, though, my body got tired.

"Ready to get out?" I asked Kristy.

"Yeah, let's eat," she replied. Kristy's dad was already grilling meat and corn on his charcoal grill, and my stomach growled in anticipation.

"Anh, do you come to the beach often?" Kristy's father asked me as he flipped the teriyaki meat on the BBQ. I noticed that my friends' parents often included me in their conversations like I was an adult. This did not happen when I got together with my parents' Vietnamese friends, who either ignored me and Jack or asked us the same questions over and over again every time we saw them, like "How old are you?" or "What grade are you in?"

"No, my parents don't like me coming to the beach," I replied.

Kristy's father looked surprised. "Why?"

"They think the ocean is dangerous, and they don't want my skin getting too dark from being out in the sun," I answered.

"But you live in Hawaii!" Kristy laughed. "What else are you supposed to do?"

"Where is your family from?" Kristy's father asked curiously.

"My parents are from Vietnam. They came here in 1975 after the war ended," I answered, giving the same generic response whenever someone asked me about my family origins. To be honest, I didn't know any more details than those basic facts because my parents never told me any more details, and people usually didn't ask me for any more follow-up questions anyway.

"Do you want a piece of chicken?" Kristy asked me.

"Yes! That smells so good," I replied as I grabbed a hot chicken drumstick marinated in BBQ sauce and spices from the plate Kristy was holding out to me. The meat was almost too hot, but as my teeth bit into it, I felt the tender meat's juice release into my mouth. Oooohhhh, it was a sensual delight. The warm breeze blowing on my still slightly wet skin contrasting with the warm explosion of tastes in my mouth made me feel so happy, inside and out. This was the best part of living in Hawaii.

Chapter 9 - Anh

1990

My parents had me work at our store on the weekends so I could keep an eye on the employees. "They'll work harder if someone from our family is at the store watching. Otherwise, they'll just be lazy," my mom told me. At least it was interesting to people-watch in Waikiki. Tourists from Asian countries were deathly afraid of the sun, which made me wonder why they even chose to vacation in Hawaii in the first place. I watched with curiosity as they tried in vain to cover up as much of their delicate skin from the intense Hawaiian rays as they could. Meanwhile, their Western counterparts worshipped the sun, parading around Waikiki with as much of their flesh exposed as possible. They were determined to change their pale white skin into shades of Kona coffee brown by the time they boarded the plane back home. But instead, they ended up burning themselves in the sun with painful shades of peeling lobster skin. This human show repeated its predictable cycle over and over again each week.

I didn't really like working at my parents' store. It didn't suit my personality or temperament to sell people things. I couldn't bring myself to feign interest in whether the haole tourist from Nebraska bought herself the blue muumuu or not, or whether she could convince her husband to buy a matching aloha shirt so they could dress up for a dinner luau that night. I was impatient with helping customers try on outfit after outfit and then decide that they didn't like any of them after all, leaving me with a pile of clothes to hang back up. The one activity I didn't mind was folding the free t-shirt table. My mom came up with a popular promotion to give away a free t-shirt for every $25 in purchases. These were not high-quality t-shirts – they were thin shirts that had large tacky designs stiffly ironed on them, but my mom had figured out the psychology of consumerism. FREE and SALE were magic words that were irresistible to a potential customer. I was amused at how excited the tourists became when they discovered they could pick out a free t-shirt from the table. They rummaged through the piles of shirts as if they had won the lottery. The t-shirt table got messed up almost every hour, so it was an endless activity to occupy my time. I picked out the shirts that needed refolding and took them back to my hangout behind the cash register. Folding t-shirts over and over into a neat pile was kind of relaxing, a way to stop my mind from worrying or thinking.

"Well aren't you a cute thing?" tourists sometimes commented to me in the same tone of voice they had just used flipping through bathing suits. When I was younger, it used to be fun hanging out at my parents' aloha store, but now I found myself getting more annoyed with tourists, the way they came to a place, purchased items to costume themselves up in, snapped photos, and then flew off on a plane back to their real lives, leaving behind a wake of trash and money. There seemed to be no way to separate the trash from the money that the tourists brought with them. Locals had to accept one with the other.

Who were the locals anyway? What did it mean to be local? Was I a local? Was my family local? I was born in Hawaii, and my family had lived here on the islands now for close to 15 years, but my "localness" was not as rich or deep as some of my other "local" friends. I didn't have aunties and uncles who lived all over the island and who had lived here for generations. I didn't know all the secret surf breaks, or hidden away beaches, or trees to pick fruit and flower from. I didn't know all the traditions that were passed down like recipes within families. My parents were no help. As long as their business made enough money to pay the bills, that was enough for them.

The one lucky thing about having my parents' store in Waikiki was that it was right across from the beach. My parents wouldn't drive me to the beach, but if I worked at their store, I had easy access to the ocean.

My mom still didn't approve of me going to the beach, but I think she has accepted my love for the ocean. I still got nervous whenever I asked her if I could go to the beach.

In the afternoon, when the sun was shining right into our store, and there was a lull between waves of customers, I asked, "Mom, can I go to the beach for a bit?"

She always shook her head and gave me a look of disapproval that conveyed, "It's dangerous out there in the sun and water," but ultimately, she sighed, "OK, you can go for an hour, but be careful!" I dashed into the dressing room to change into my bathing suit and ran across Kalakaua Avenue to the beachside. Thankfully there was a boogie board rental stand and wave break right in front of my parent's shop.

"Can I rent a boogie board?" I asked the beefy Hawaiian dude manning the rental booth under the shade of the umbrella stand. He was wearing a tank top and had a picture of a young boy tattooed on his right shoulder.

"Ten dollars one hour. Leave your ID," he replied in a thick local accent.

"I don't have a driver's license yet. But I can leave you my school ID card," I offered.

"That works. OK, you can grab the blue board. You want fins too?"

"Nah, just the board," I told him. Fins cost an extra five dollars an hour to rent, and if I kicked hard enough, I could catch the waves without them and save my money to rent a board again next time. I grabbed the board, strapped the leash around my wrist, and headed down the beach to the water. I could already feel a smile creeping up on my face when I got near the water. I looked out towards the horizon to see what the conditions looked like. Some days it was flat and glassy and not worth renting a board because there were no waves to catch. Other days, the waves were too big and choppy, even for Waikiki, and I didn't trust my amateur wave-riding skills to manage them. Today was a perfect day. The waves were medium-sized and breaking slowly, providing a slowly rising surface to glide across. I jumped onto my board into the water and started kicking and paddling my way out to the waves. I loved how easy it was to go from being a bored teenager in my parents' store on land to being a happy sea creature moving in the water in less than five minutes. This tiny little boogie board break was called Walls, aptly named for the concrete seawall that stretched out from the beach into the water, providing a platform to take in the ocean view that stretched from Diamond Head to Waikiki Beach. The Wall was also a popular place for people to jump off into the water.

I reached a distance out where sets of waves began breaking enough to catch a swell and ride it. I turned my boogie board around and waited patiently for the right wave. Waves came in groups, called sets. I let others catch the first one or two waves of a set. By the time you rode a wave in, you normally didn't have enough time to paddle back out and catch another wave in that same set, so it's important to choose a particular wave in a set. The nice thing about sets was that if you didn't catch a wave, there was usually another wave right behind it. Nature was always giving you multiple tries.

Off in the distance, I saw the water start rising, the earliest sign of a swell forming. The bodyboarders in the water paddled into position, each one jockeying for the spot they thought would give them the highest probability of catching a wave and riding it for as long as possible. The first wave in the set was a nice one, and I watched as many of the bodyboarders around me turned themselves around to catch it, clearing the water of almost half of the people out there. A second wave approached, and the remaining riders who did not attempt to catch the first wave or were not successful with that attempt positioned themselves again. I continued to wait patiently. By the time the third wave in the set started swelling in the distance, I had the water mostly to myself. I paddled, aiming to position myself directly in front of the tallest peak section of the wave where it would break first, allowing me to ride the entire length of the wave face. It was a beautiful wave, strong and majestic. My heart pumped in anticipation of my encounter with this moving wall of water that was approaching me and inviting me to join it in dance. I kicked and paddled hard, trying to gather enough speed to join the wave on its course. And then I felt it, the buoyant lift of the wave as it gathered me up in its arms the way a dancer lifted his partner up in the air in exultation. I couldn't help a smile from spilling over my face as I stopped exerting my own energy and surrendered to the force of the wave beneath me. I turned my board slightly to the right so I could ride along the smooth surface of the wave as it broke behind me and carried me to shore. I had the whole wave to myself. I reached out my hand to glide it across the golden surface of the water, which was sparkling diamonds from the reflection of the sun. I felt so happy and free. As the wave crumbled and petered out near shore, I turned my board to dismount the wave and paddled back out to catch another. It was addicting. The high I felt from riding a wave, literally moving with the energy of water, was irresistible. I caught wave after wave during my session that afternoon, ultimately deciding it was time to go in when my belly started getting irritated from all the chafing with the board. I returned the board to the rental stand, showered off and changed back into my regular clothes, and returned to my parents' store.

"Anh! You were gone for so long. I was worried about you!" My mom shouted at me as soon as I returned to the store.

"I'm sorry, I lost track of time," I replied. "I'll go fold some t-shirts," I told her as I made my way to a pile of rumpled t-shirts on the free t-shirts table.

Chapter 10 - Anh

1991

"Anh, I really like what you're doing with this piece," Mrs. Rose commented on a waterscape I was working on in her class. "You should think about submitting it to the art show." My high school art teacher Mrs. Rose was the one who introduced me to watercolor painting. I had never painted before. Mrs. Rose encouraged me to develop my work. "Let the water move you and the color. The art of watercolor is letting the water do its magic," she would say. "Don't work so hard at it. Play with it. Relax. Let it flow." She spent time with me after school and on the weekends, and she gave me tips and advice on watercolor painting. My parents were much more focused on me doing well in my academic studies rather than pursuing frivolous interests like art. The only extracurricular activity that they approved of, and were willing to pay for, was my piano lessons. I endured my piano lessons with the same discipline I approached my Japanese language kanji tables at school, something to learn and master, but not something I particularly enjoyed.

With painting, it was different. I was mesmerized by the infinite shades of color and shadow that I could create and mix and blend together. The multiple hues of blue and green and gold on my palette plate reminded me of the rainbow of subtle colors in the ocean that constantly moved back and forth as light and water twinkled with one another. With watercolor painting, the strokes did not have to be precise, and mistakes were welcomed as happy accidents. In piano, an F sharp was an F sharp. Being close to F sharp was still not right. With painting, there was no right answer, and being close enough was sometimes even better than achieving what you thought was right. I loved being able to change how dark or light something was just by adjusting the amount of liquid or paint on my brush. Playing with the water and colors and light was like dancing on the paper, without having to memorize a pre-set series of steps. It was about feeling where the water and the color wanted to move through my body and out from my hand holding the brush onto the canvas, like my body was a tube of paint pouring itself onto the fresh surface.

Watercolors gave me a freedom I did not experience anywhere else in my life. Playing in the ocean was like playing with color, was like playing with beauty. Playing was not something my parents valued. Work. Money. Education. These were their mantras. I tried my best to pledge allegiance to their values too. I worked hard at my studies, and then I lost myself playing in my paintings, the ocean, and my paintings of the ocean.

CHAPTER 11- XUAN

1991

"Mom, can I wear your *áo dài* dress as my Halloween costume?" Anh asked me as she came into the kitchen holding up my traditional red wedding dress from a hanger.

"What?" I ask, confused by her question.

"I can't find anything in my closet to wear for Halloween tomorrow, so I looked in your closet and found this red *áo dài* dress. I can dress up with this Asian costume."

Out of all the American holidays our children had been introduced to in this country, Halloween was the strangest. Why would people open up their homes to strangers and potential robbers who were already wearing costumes to disguise their identity, just to hand out candy to children? I did not know how to respond. Anh was holding up my red wedding *áo dài* in her hands, asking if she could wear it as a Halloween costume. For a Vietnamese girl and woman, an *áo dài*, the traditional Vietnamese dress that was usually tailor-made to custom fit your body, and worn with long white silk pants underneath, was a special item. I remember how excited I was when my mother took me to the tailor to get measured for my first *áo dài* dress for Tết when I was around five years old. I got to choose the color and pattern of the fabric – light pink with a golden trim and flowers decorating it. I was so proud of it and pulled it out to look at it every day, waiting for the special day to wear it. When she was young, I had wanted to get Anh her own *áo dài* dress, but I did not sew well and didn't know anyone else in Hawaii who could make it either.

"Why don't you try it on and see how it looks?" I answered, curious to see how Anh would look in my wedding dress.

"OK," she replied and went back to her room to try it on. A few minutes later, she came back wearing the same shorts and t-shirt she had been wearing earlier.

"What happened?" I asked.

"It didn't fit me after all. I could barely fit my arms into it, it was too small," she answered.

It surprised me that my 16-year-old daughter could not fit into a dress I wore on my wedding day. Was Anh really that much bigger than I was?

"I'll go look in Dad's closet and see if I can find some old shirts to dress up like a farmer then," Anh said as she walked off.

I went back to slicing cucumbers for dinner, but I couldn't stop thinking with sadness about how much Vietnamese culture had been lost to my American teenage daughter. Anh looked at my wedding dress as a potential Halloween costume, something that she thought would make her different than who she was. She was clearly telling me that she did not see herself as a Vietnamese girl. An *áo dài* was the same to her as a farmer's plaid shirt and overalls, just a costume, not an identity. She was Vietnamese, but growing up in America had made her forget that.

Chapter 12 - Anh

1992

We were learning about the American Civil War in my AP US History class, about the differences in ideology and culture between the North and the South, and I found myself wanting to learn more about Vietnam's civil war too. I've asked my parents many times to tell me more about the war, but they never wanted to talk about it much. I wanted to understand what their life was like in Vietnam, but they didn't give me much information.

"Dad, what do you remember about the war?" I asked my father one day.

"Which one? There have been too many," my father replied.

"The Vietnam War," I reply, confused.

"What was there to remember? It's over now."

"Did you see any fighting?"

"I heard bombs exploding all the time."

"Were you scared?"

"There was no time to be scared. We just had to keep on living. Too many questions. Enough already. You don't need to know. Go do your homework."

I was sometimes annoyed by how my parents determined what I needed to know or not. They never told me anything important. They hid everything that happened to them behind an impenetrable door, leaving them as one-dimensional as the cartoon characters I saw on TV. It was hard for me to understand my parents, and I was frustrated by how they didn't even try to understand me.

Talking to Mom about the war revealed even less information. My mom always answered, "I don't remember what happened. It all happened so long ago."

In my history class, I learned how Hawaii became an official part of the United States. I decided to do my term paper on the overthrow of the Hawaiian monarchy. In elementary school, I remembered touring Iolani Palace, the royal family's residence, marveling at the beautiful koa wood furniture and decorative capes and headpieces fashioned out of thousands of colorful bird feathers. I was shocked to learn of Hawaii's history with the US. When I read about Queen Liliʻuokalani, the last reigning monarch of the Hawaiian kingdom, and how she was overthrown in a coup d'état in 1893, which eventually led to Hawaii becoming annexed and an official territory of the United States, my blood started to boil in anger. It had only been a century or so ago that this land belonged to another country, another government, another people. My own parents sometimes remarked that their own country had been taken away from them. Could countries change hands so easily? What happened to the people who lived there?

I was angry at the injustice of it all and wondered how people in power could so easily use their positions to do whatever they wanted without regard to others. Was it all because of money and power? In a strange way, even though my own family had left Vietnam because they did not want to live under Communist rule, I felt a sense of pride in how my motherland of Vietnam had managed to defeat outside powers such as the French, Chinese, and even the Americans to maintain their own autonomy. Our country Vietnam was still ruled by Vietnamese, even if Vietnamese-Americans like my family and myself no longer lived there. If the Americans had won the war in Vietnam, would Vietnam have had the same fate as Hawaii, eventually being controlled by a larger superpower? Conversely, had American protection and economic development helped to improve life in Hawaii and make it possible for people like my family to find refuge and start a new life here? It was a complicated debate that I could safely explore in the confines of a term paper rather than questioning my own family's path across the Pacific Ocean from Vietnam to Hawaii. For now, all I could conclude was that there were no easy answers to these difficult questions. Maybe that's why my parents stopped trying to answer them.

Chapter 13 - Anh

1992

It's been almost two weeks since I've been discharged from the psychiatric hospital, but I haven't gone back to school yet. "Your friends are asking about you," my younger brother Jack mentions to me when he arrives home from school. "What do you want me to tell them?"

I haven't even thought about that yet. What am I going to tell people when I go back to school? That I spent two weeks in the mental hospital, that I lost my mind, and am now being drugged so that I can return to the land of the sane?

"What do they already know?" I ask to assess the situation.

"Not much. I've been vague. I told them that you were in the hospital, didn't tell them which one." I know that I haven't always been the most gracious older sister. I often take advantage of my little brother's loyalty. He is the type of guy who will always defend his family from shame or gossip, even if it were true.

"I don't know yet. I'll think about it," I reply.

"Just don't say anything. You don't have to tell them anything. It's none of their business," he goes on. I feel a twinge of tenderness towards Jack. And then, out of nowhere, an angry thought floats through my mind that he is just trying to protect himself from the shame of his older sister being in Kahi Mohala.

Kahi Mohala is the main psychiatric hospital on the island of Oahu. Everyone refers to it as just "Kahi" and it is known as the place where crazy people are sent. People often jokingly ribbed each other with comments like, "You need to go to Kahi!" Never in my life did I imagine I would be a patient at Kahi Mohala.

"Why?" I snap back. "Are you embarrassed about me? Do you want me to just hide out at home forever, so you don't ever have to tell your friends the truth that your sister is crazy and went to the looney bin?"

"Whoa, what are you talking about?" Jack looks genuinely shocked at my response, and then in the next instant, I see him brace himself with that steely demeanor I now recognize when people respond to my attacks. I hate it. It makes me feel like a monster. People can't stand looking at me or talking to me. It makes me even more angry, as if now the only option I have is to blow fire on them like they expect, so they will go away and leave me alone.

"Get out of my room!" I yell at him.

Jack shakes his head and backs away from my doorway. He doesn't understand what my problem is, why I'm so mean to him. "Here are the homework packets I picked up for you from school," he mutters, leaving a folder with a stack of papers at my door as he walks away to his own room.

With a dramatic flourish, I pick up the folder, take out the stack of papers stacked neatly and throw them up in the air, littering my previously clean room with a messy array of papers. Then for good measure, I slam my door as hard as I can to clearly send the message that I do not want to be disturbed. In a final effort, I fling myself on the bed and cover my head with my pillow. My ears are ringing, and my head is throbbing as if my heart is pounding in the walls of my skull rather than my chest. I can't handle this. I just want to make it all go away, to go to sleep and not have to wake up to this nightmare.

Bà nội knocks quietly on my door, "Come here, con, let me rub the wind out of your body, that will help you get better," she says. Every time Jack or I catch a fever, Bà nội gives us a *cạo gió*, a back scrubbing to literally bring the wind out of our bodies. Bà nội always soothes me, and I nod my head to let her know that she can come in. She sits down next to me in my bed, and I take off my shirt to expose my bare back to her. Bà nội uses a piece of ginger root dipped in menthol oil to rub my back vigorously. The long, brisk strokes Bà nội makes on my back are both comforting and uncomfortable, leaving long red abrasions on my skin, which Bà nội says are a good sign that the wind causing my fever or illness is rising to the surface to be released. Whenever I get sick, both my mom and Bà nội pray to Buddha to let my illness be passed on to them. I wonder if they would want whatever had befallen me these past few weeks. It's not something I would wish on anyone.

Chapter 14 - Xuan

1992

When I was a little girl, my mother took me to see the fortune teller. Whenever my mother had a worry or concern, she would consult this woman for advice or reassurance about the future. I recalled that the old lady sat silently on the ground, closing her eyes as she read our futures. She had told me that I would journey far in my life, but that my life would be a short one. My mother was angry with that fortune teller and cursed her for sharing such a sorrowful prediction. “Fortune tellers know they’re not supposed to tell people bad news like that, forget what she said,” my mother told me. But I had never forgotten what she said, and the first half of her prediction had already become true – I had journeyed far away from Vietnam. Was my own death now imminent? The old lady had told me and my mother that dreams were very powerful, and they were often important messages from beyond. “Pay attention to your dreams,” the old lady heeded.

I have been worrying a lot about Anh, who is now finally out of the hospital, but still not back to her usual self. I worry that Anh will never get completely better again. I remember those people in Vietnam who were not quite right in their heads. Their families kept them locked up inside their homes, but they inevitably found their way out onto the streets, and wandered aimlessly through the neighborhood, talking to whoever would pay them attention, not making any sense at all. Eventually, someone from the neighborhood walked them back to their homes and returned them to their families. Sometimes desperate family members tied these sick people to the bed or a tree like a dog so that they could not venture away and get lost.

I try to get these images out of my head. Anh will be different. That Japanese doctor in the hospital told me and Long that Anh has bipolar disorder and that this is a very treatable illness. I went to the bookstore to try and find books to read about mental illness and bipolar disorder, but my English was not good enough to understand all of the words in the thick books. It felt like I was trying to understand something complicated in a foreign language. So I do my best to remember what Anh's doctor told us. If Anh takes her medication, she will get better and be able to go back to school and live a normal life. I hold onto those words. A normal life. That is all I want for my daughter. For her to go to college, find a good job, get married, have children, and have a normal life. Not the crazy life that I have gone through, being given away by my own mother, growing up in a country torn apart by war, fleeing the land where I was born to start life over again in a foreign place. Long and I work hard so that our children can have a better life than us. We do everything we can to prepare them for a bright future. Yet our daughter has ended up sick, very sick. Is Buddha punishing me for leaving my parents behind in Vietnam and thinking of myself before them? Are my children being punished for my bad decisions? I pray to Phật Bà Quan Thế Âm for her compassion and guidance.

Long and I both feel the gradual erosion of our ties to our motherland. Our children are growing up more American than Vietnamese. The loss is slow and not easily noticed on a daily basis, but the sand slips away underneath our feet each time the ocean climbs up on shore, drawing back an inch or two of shoreline each year. Without seawalls to protect it, one's own culture slowly slips away like grains of sand in an hourglass until one day, nothing is left except the empty place where something once existed.

When we first arrived in Honolulu, our family celebrated *Tết*, or Lunar New Year, each year with the traditional glutinous rice cakes *bánh chưng* and visits to the Buddhist temple *chùa*. But as the kids got older and were less willing to come along to such events, we stopped insisting on it. Soon, the louder, more effectively advertised American holidays like Thanksgiving and Christmas drowned out our traditional Vietnamese holidays. Anh and Jack became more excited about trick-or-treating and receiving Christmas presents than going to pray at temple. We had to surrender to the larger forces in our lives. We did not have the heart or the energy to hold onto something that we had already lost. Reminding ourselves of how much we lost over and over again was too painful. We thought it would be easier to just try and forget and move on.

But I find that as much as I try to forget Vietnam, I cannot. The memory of leaving my parents behind still weighs heavily in my heart. It is strange how my memory changes with time. I cannot even clearly recall how my family celebrated *Tết* when I was growing up in Vietnam, but now that I am thousands of miles away in a foreign land, I imagine a table piled high with all of my favorite foods and colorful flowers and the excitement of receiving red *lì xì* envelopes with small gifts of money from my parents and elders. I am ashamed at my lack of cooking skills, especially when a wife's culinary skills are highly praised. When I try to make *chả giò*, my spring rolls always turn out messier and puffier than Chi Lien's. The wrappers on mine often break apart and spill the contents when they are dropped into the frying pan. When Long expressed interest in marrying me, I did not try to hide my deficiency in the kitchen. I confessed to him that I was not a good cook and that if we got married, I would not be a stellar performer in the kitchen. I was nervous to receive his response, wondering whether my admission would turn him away, and how my mother would berate me for being so foolish to admit such a thing to a future husband. But I did not feel good about deceiving others, especially regarding my own talents and abilities. Better to admit to the truth now than to be accused of advertising false goods in the future. Besides, my Buddhist beliefs made me believe that any lie would always come back to me anyway, whether in this lifetime or future ones. There is no avoiding the consequences of one's actions, good or bad. This is just how karma works.

I was relieved when Long laughed heartily at my admission of my culinary deficiencies. "As long as you nourish me in our bedroom, we can hire a cook to prepare our meals," he replied. In Vietnam, it was common practice, if a family could afford it, to hire someone to help cook. After we married, Long was true to his word, and we hired Bà Binh, an elderly lady who had lost her family, to help prepare meals for us. Bà Binh was an excellent cook. Her *cá kho* braised fish and *canh chua* sweet and sour soup were exquisite. Sometimes I was so amazed at how delicious the dishes were that I watched Bà Binh and tried to learn how she could create such savory flavors from the simple ingredients she had at hand. But every time I tried to repeat what I had watched Bà Binh so effortlessly put together, it never turned out quite the same.

Long and I had only been married and living together for less than a year when we left for America. In Hawaii, we barely had enough money to buy groceries for the week, much less hire someone to cook for us. Besides, there were not that many Vietnamese refugees who ended up in Hawaii. I found myself dragged back into the linoleum-floored kitchen in America, feeling even more incapable than I did in Vietnam. The grocery stores and ingredients here are foreign to me, along with the appliances I am supposed to use to prepare these ingredients. But I am not a woman who is too proud to do what she needs to do in order to fulfill my family duties. I pride myself on being practical. I do not need to prove myself in the kitchen, all I need to do is provide my family with enough calories to get them through the day. I learn how to make fried rice with Spam, and how to marinate chicken with bottled teriyaki sauce. I believe that my ancestors are proud of me for being so resourceful. Having enough American food to put on the table to feed our children is better than digging through Vietnamese soil littered with undetonated mines and war scraps.

Chapter 15 - Anh

1992

"I don't want to go see Dr. Tanaka," I tell my parents. I don't want any reminders of my time being in the psychiatric hospital.

"You have an appointment with Dr. Tanaka today. We have to show up for your appointment," my mother reasons with me. "She will tell us what we need to do next."

"Do you think she'll let me stop taking this horrible medication?" I ask.

"Maybe, we have to go to see what she says."

"Alright, let's go then," I sigh.

Dr. Tanaka's office is in a brown, wooden two-story building adjacent to the hospital. The waiting room is clean and simply furnished with an assortment of magazines on the end tables. There is already another family sitting there, a mom and a boy who looks about ten years old. I have never been to a psychiatrist's office before, and I wonder curiously what brings other people to this place. It's not like the dentist's office, where no one seems particularly interested to know what other people are doing there, most likely to get their teeth cleaned or a cavity filled. There is no shame in sitting in a dentist's office. Here, I feel strangely anxious about who I might run into and morbidly curious at the same time about what brings others to this same shameful and awkward place.

The door leading to the offices behind the reception area opens, and a young office assistant who doesn't look much older than me steps out with a clipboard in her hands and calls out, "Anh Nguyen?" My parents and I both stand up, unsure who is supposed to respond. "You can all come back with me," the assistant gestures to us helpfully. She measures my height and weight and leads us back to another simple, sparsely furnished room with a large desk and a handful of black metal chairs arranged in a semi-circle around the front of the desk. There is a wilting plant on the desk that looks like it needs a good watering and perhaps more sunlight. My parents and I sit stiffly in the chairs, which seem intentionally designed to make it impossible to relax.

After what seems like half an hour, but likely is only five minutes or so, there is a firm knock on the door and in enters Dr. Tanaka, the doctor from the hospital. She is dressed in a professional grey skirt and a crisp pink button-down blouse.

"Hello, it's nice to see you again Anh," she says, as she reaches out her hand to shake my hand and my parents' hands.

"Anh, how have you been since leaving the hospital?" It has been 2 weeks since I left the hospital.

"The medicine makes me tired," I answer. "The Lithium is helping me feel less angry and irritable, but I don't like how it makes me feel like there is a cotton candy cloud wrapped around my head. And instead of the cloud being light and fluffy, it makes my head heavy and weighed down. I know my anger is still under there, but it can't seem to rise above this pressure pushing it down.

"That is common with Lithium, but hopefully, your body will get used to it after a few more weeks, and you won't feel as tired," the doctor explains.

"I also feel like I've gained twenty pounds," I add.

Dr. Tanaka looks at her chart and nods, "Yes, you have gained 8 pounds since you left the hospital..." Dr. Tanaka sighs as she flips through some more papers, "...and 17 pounds since you first entered the hospital. Weight gain, unfortunately, is a common side effect of Lithium and all the bipolar medications actually. There's nothing we can really do about it."

"How long will she need to take this medication?" my mother asks the doctor. "She is doing much better now."

"Yes, I agree Anh seems to be doing a lot better than before. But with bipolar disorder, I do not recommend stopping the medication right away, or else she could have another episode again."

"You mean, I have to take these awful pills for the rest of my life?" I ask in shock. I had not even contemplated the thought that I would need to continue taking this medication. Half the reason I agreed to come today is that I was under the impression that today's check-up with the doctor would be a clearance for me to stop taking the medication. My plan is to go back to school next week, and I can't imagine doing my homework with this heavy weight pushing down on my brain.

"No, not necessarily. But I would definitely continue taking them for now. There is a very high risk for relapse if you stop your bipolar medication," the doctor continues to calmly explain. "I know I explained to you what bipolar disorder is while you were in the hospital, but sometimes it's helpful to go over it again now that you're back at home. Do you remember anything I told you about bipolar disorder?"

I've already decided that I've been misdiagnosed. I just had a small breakdown from not getting enough sleep and being stressed out preparing for the art show. I don't believe what the doctor is saying about me having bipolar disorder and needing to continue taking medication. I feel fine now, back to my usual self, and once I stop taking the Lithium, I'll feel even better.

My parents are quiet in response to Dr. Tanaka's question, the typical Asian response to authority.

"Well, let me explain it to you again," Dr. Tanaka patiently responds as she goes over a basic explanation of bipolar disorder, how it usually first appears in adolescence, and fortunately, how amenable it is to treatment, even if the medications used to treat it do tend to have some significant side effects. I instinctively stop listening to what the doctor is saying, almost as if I've hit the mute button and can see the doctor's lips moving but can't hear anything she's saying. When the doctor finishes, she asks, "Any questions?" to which my parents and I shake our heads.

"I know that's a lot of information to take in, but I'll continue to see Anh and help your family through the process..." the doctor starts up again, and I push the mute button in my brain to silence her. "...Now I'd like to spend some time alone with Anh, if that's OK with her," Dr. Tanaka continues.

My parents all of a sudden stand up, which prompts me to do the same, but Dr. Tanaka says to me, "You stay Anh, I'd like to spend some time with you." My parents exit the room, and I'm left alone in the office with Dr. Tanaka. I push the button to unmute the doctor. I don't want her to think I'm crazy and need to be re-hospitalized or anything. It's important to answer her questions correctly and pretend like everything is going just fine.

Dr. Tanaka sits there quietly for a few moments, just looking at me with a slight smile on her lips, wondering how to start. Having someone just sit there and stare at me makes me extremely uncomfortable, and I start squirming in my chair.

"How has it been for you being back home?" Dr. Tanaka finally breaks the silence with a simple query.

"Fine. I've been staying home from school, and my grandma's been taking care of me." I answer in as few words as I can.

"How do you feel about going back to school next week?"

I squirm again. "OK." I actually am very anxious about going back to school, about handling the schoolwork, about seeing my friends, and having to answer everyone's questions about what happened.

"Do your friends know what happened?"

"About what?"

"About you being in the hospital?"

"No, not really. A few of them have tried calling me, but I haven't called them back."

"What will you say when you see them again?"

"I don't know, I'll figure it out." I've been avoiding thinking about how I'm going to handle my return to school. It overwhelms me whenever I think about it, so I try not to think about it.

"I remember you were painting right before you came to the hospital," Dr. Tanaka tries again, trying to find a way to get me to relax. "Have you painted at all since you've gotten home?"

"No, my parents cleaned up all my supplies. And the art show I was working on is over, so there's no point."

"You don't need a reason to paint. That's the beauty of art, right, there's really no point to it, it's just beautiful."

"You're right," I agree. I am surprised to hear the doctor talk about something completely unrelated to bipolar disorder or medication or my illness or the hospital.

"Do you paint?" I ask Dr. Tanaka.

"No, I'm not a painter," Dr. Tanaka laughs softly, "but I do like art. I'd love to see some of your work sometime."

I nod my head slightly, "Sure."

Another awkward silence.

"Can I go now?" I finally ask.

Dr. Tanaka smiles again. "Of course, I'll see you again next month, take care."

Chapter 16 - Anh

1992

I'm anxious about returning to school. As it happens, my first class Monday morning is the same English class I had my "episode" in a month ago. Jack had brought me homework packets from all of my classes so that I could keep up with my assignments, but I haven't worked on them at all. After the hospital, I spent most of my time at home lying in bed staring at the ceiling or watching television, trying to avoid thinking about all the responsibilities that awaited me when I returned to school.

Last night I briefly looked over the syllabus for my classes to have some idea of what subject we were going to discuss. My English class lists "Personal Essays" as the topic of the week. Oh, God.

I arrive a few minutes early for the class, hoping to slip in unnoticed somewhere in the back. But as soon as the class bell rings, Mr. McLaren loudly announces, "Welcome back, Anh, we've all missed you!" Everyone turns around to look at me, and I feel so exposed that I want to shrink into the size of an ant and crawl away into the cracks in the walls.

"Alright, class, let's get started. This week we are going to be working on your own personal essays. We've been studying the styles of various writers, and now I want you all to have an opportunity to experiment with your own writing voices. We'll talk about brainstorming and deciding what you want to write about and some different techniques you can use to get you started," Mr. McLaren explains.

This is an assignment that I normally would embrace. I enjoy opportunities to express myself freely rather than trying to interpret someone else's work, making up meanings and metaphors into a persuasive argument that the authors themselves probably don't care a damn about. But today, I feel as excited as a rock by the assignment. I feel numb, almost dead. That's how the rest of the day goes. Every teacher in every class makes it a point to remind everyone that this is my first day back in class after being gone for a month, and I cringe at the attention.

During my lunch break, I find my way to the cafeteria, grab some lunch, and sit down in the area where my friends and I normally sit. I'm the first one there.

My friend Lauren finally shows up and sits down next to me. "Hi, Anh. It's so good to see you. How are *you*?" she asks, sincerely concerned.

I can't hold it in anymore. I feel like I'm going to break down and start crying right there, and that's the last thing I want to do.

"Can we go somewhere to talk? I don't want to be here right now," I ask her.

"Sure, let's go sit by the Lily Pond," Lauren suggests, already picking up her backpack and tray. That is one of the privileges of being in the Academy, you can eat your lunch anywhere on campus, not just in the cafeteria.

The Lily Pond is the physical and spiritual center of the Punahou campus. It is where fresh spring water was discovered by the missionaries who founded the school in 1841, and it is the place where all life on campus and beyond returns to and springs from. The pond is knee-deep and covered in lotus petals and blooms. When I peer inside the murky waters, I can see tadpoles, fish, and the occasional turtle swimming around. In the middle of the pond, there is a small island with a single hala tree, the school's crest, growing on it. The island is set off a few feet from the banks of the shore and requires a good running start and leap of faith to land on it. Leaping, of course, is prohibited by school rules, which makes it a constant temptation for students. The hala tree has a majestic form. Its roots are exposed, serving as a reminder that one always comes from and depends on one's roots, even after one has blossomed into a beautiful grown specimen. The Lily Pond is situated right next to the school chapel, in fact, it looks like the chapel is built right into the pond itself. I love how the water and building touch each other's edges seamlessly, one extending directly into the other without a break in contact. I often go to the Lily Pond as a quiet place to eat lunch or spend time in the warm sunshine.

Lauren is one of my closer friends. "I've tried calling you, but you haven't returned my calls. I've been worried about you," Lauren says.

"I'm sorry I didn't call you back. It's been such a blur, and I've been such a mess. I don't even know where to start," I begin. "It's so weird being back at school. I'm sure everyone's looking at me and talking about how I had to go to Kahi."

"No, it's not like that. People know you were in Kahi, but that was ages ago, most of them don't even mention it anymore." Lauren tries to reassure me. "They had an assembly speaker come talk to everyone about mental illness and suicide. They told us how common it is for teenagers to get depressed."

"I wasn't depressed or suicidal," I respond in shock. Is that what everyone thought had happened?

"What did happen then?"

I pause. I'm not sure if I am ready to go all into it right then. I'm not even sure I know what happened. I can barely explain it to myself coherently, much less to someone else.

"I'm still not quite sure," I finally answer honestly, and after a pause, I dare ask, "So what did you think about the Assembly speaker?" I want to get a sense of what Lauren thinks of these things.

"I thought about you. I wondered what was going on, if there was anything I could have done differently to help you."

I am touched by my friend's sincere words. "Thanks, but I don't think there was. I still don't even know what happened. My doctor tells me I have something called bipolar disorder. But I don't know, that sounds really serious. How can she be sure?"

"I think one of my cousins has bipolar disorder. Our family never talks about it, but he once told me that he had it," Lauren continues.

"And how is he now?" I ask.

"I don't know, he's older, so we've kind of lost touch. I know he went off to college, but I don't know much else."

There is a long awkward silence. Lauren finally breaks it, "Do you need any help catching up on your work?"

I can't stop the tears that well up in my eyes and spill down my cheeks. "Thank you. It helps to just talk about it," I reply as I reach out to hug my friend.

Chapter 17 - Anh

1992

I look at myself in the mirror and grimace at the unsightly bulge growing around my belly. I turn to look at myself in profile, and I do not like what I see. My pants have started fitting tightly. This morning I can't button my jeans which makes me especially depressed. My medication is turning me into a fat slob. Dr. Tanaka is right: I have gotten more used to taking Lithium, but I can't get used to my new body.

I used to pride myself on my skinniness. Like most Asian girls, I am naturally blessed with a trim figure and don't really have to work at staying slim. I am used to eating as much as I want without gaining weight. Now, it seems like I gain weight just by looking at food. Even if I don't eat anything all day, my stomach feels bloated, and the number on the scale continues to climb every time I step onto it. I have gained over thirty pounds since I started taking Lithium, which is a lot on my small frame!

That does it, I decide. I'm going to stop taking my Lithium. Getting fat is making me more depressed than my supposed bipolar disorder. My mom has been giving me my medication twice a day for the past two months, but recently she's been trusting me to take it by myself. Plus, I feel back to my normal self. I'm back to school, and everyone seems to have forgotten about my hospitalization earlier this year. When I saw Dr. Tanaka last week, even she commented on how pleased she was with my progress. I asked her if I could stop my medication, but again Dr. Tanaka reiterated to me that this would put me at risk of relapse. I am willing to take the *possible* risk because the Lithium is *definitely* making me feel horrible about my body. I'm the type of person who once I make a decision, I follow through with it, without looking back.

I change out of my too-tight jeans and choose something looser to slip into. I am smart enough to know that I will need to continue to pretend that I am still taking my medication so my parents won't notice. So every day, at breakfast and dinner, I go through the motions of putting the Lithium tablet into my mouth and pretending to swallow it, then excuse myself to spit it back up in the toilet. "Bye-bye, little white pill, I hope you make the fishies happy," I say as I wave to the medication and watch it swirl and disappear down the toilet bowl.

After I stop taking my Lithium, I notice the heaviness in my head lifting, and I start having more energy. It was definitely the right decision to stop taking the medicine. I have so much energy that I can do all my homework and still not feel tired at night. Plus, I am writing again! The ideas and inspiration are just flowing out of me. I scribble in my journal furiously, letting the words spill out like running water. Every night I stay up later than the previous night until one morning, I see the sky start turning light and realize it's time to go to school, and I haven't slept at all yet. Jack walks by my room on his way to the bathroom and is surprised to find me all dressed and ready for school nearly an hour before we have to leave the house. "Excited for school, are we?" he snickers casually. I've been nicer to him recently. I haven't been as irritable lately, so I offered to help him with the art for a science poster he is working on. I don't have time to look up at Jack's comment, so he continues on his way down the hallway. He's now used to my unpredictable moods and has learned that it is best to just ignore or avoid me.

I am restless with energy. I am sitting at my desk with the lamp on. I normally have neat handwriting, but this morning the words and thoughts coming from my brain are pouring out so fast that I have to use a made-up shorthand to keep up. All night I've been receiving messages and images about a huge wave of water that is making its way across the Pacific Ocean from Vietnam to Hawaii. I've made the calculations that it will arrive on the South shore of Oahu in a few hours. I feel panicked and sweaty, my heart is pounding. I need to warn my family so that we can evacuate to higher ground and not get drowned by the tsunami.

I rush down the hallway to find Jack in the bathroom. "Get your stuff together, we have to go to the top of the mountain. There's a big tsunami coming! You go tell Mom and Dad, I'll go tell Bà nội."

"Wait, what is going on? What are you talking about?" Jack asks me. He is splashing himself awake at the bathroom sink, and his face is still dripping with water as he looks up at me.

"I've done all the calculations. Look here," I say as I gesture to the notes in my journal. "There is going to be a large tsunami coming across the Pacific Ocean with 50-foot waves. It will wash over everything with large floods. We need to get to higher ground," I explain urgently.

Jack ponders my animated declarations. Living on an island, tsunami warnings and occasional evacuations to higher elevations are infrequent, but not entirely unheard of either. During one particularly serious warning several years ago, our entire family evacuated to Dr. Tran's house on top of Mariner's Ridge. School was canceled, and all the Vietnamese families we knew had gathered together to watch the news on TV. People brought over food and drinks and what had started out as an emergency warning turned into an impromptu social gathering.

"What do you mean you've done all the calculations? Is that also what the news is saying?" Jack asks me. He goes into the living room to flip on the TV to check out what is really going on. If there is a tsunami evacuation going on, then it would surely be broadcast on all the local TV stations. But when he turns on the TV to channel 4, Kai Takahashi, the local anchor of KITV 4, is just going through the weather report, "Clear skies, mostly sunny, with trade winds 5-15 miles per hour out of the southeast. Now let's move onto the surf report," he continues on in his calm voice. I wonder why people in Hawaii are so interested in the weather report when it is practically the same thing every day. Jack listens intently to the newscast, but there is no mention of any type of storm causing an approaching tsunami. Jack flips to Channel 9 to catch another local station just to make sure. On this channel, they are moving onto a local-interest piece about an elderly Japanese woman who owns the largest private collection of silk kimono robes outside of Japan. Again, no mention of an approaching tsunami wave.

The news stations are probably not covering this news to avoid creating traffic for their own families to gain safe ground. I am trying to press the urgency of the situation onto my family.

"I told you we have to go to the top of the Ko'olaus, the highest point on the island. I saw it coming, it's going to be a big one. Everything will be flooded, many people will die. We are being punished for our sins. God is very angry at us. He will only save the people who listen to him. You have to listen to me before it's too late," I continue.

"Anh, stop! There is no tsunami coming," my brother tries to talk some sense into me. My parents are now also in the living room, watching the news on TV to assess the situation for themselves. My father is shaking his head and furrowing his eyebrows. My mom looks like she's already been hit by a tsunami wave of anxiety.

"*Con ơi*," she says, and she approaches me, but I will not allow myself to be calmed or even touched. I have to stay focused on delivering this message. They don't understand the danger. I start pacing back and forth furiously like a caged animal. "Why won't you believe me? We are all about to die. I'm trying to save us. I'm not going to let it happen."

Chapter 18 - Dr. Tanaka

1992

Dr. Tanaka scanned through the list of names of new admissions from the night before. Anh Nguyen, 17 years old, was in room 8A. She wondered what happened. She had just seen Anh in her office not too long ago, and Anh had been doing well. Dr. Tanaka quickly flipped through the admission paperwork to get an idea of the situation. The ER notes read, *17-year-old Asian female brought in by police from home. Family reports that client has bipolar disorder and was taking her medication as prescribed. Patient presented in a manic episode with pressured speech, agitation, and delusional thoughts about a tsunami coming. Family reports client has not been sleeping well for past several weeks. Urine toxicology negative. All other labs normal. Lithium level <0.3. Medically clear for discharge to psychiatric hospital.*

Dr. Tanaka noted that Anh's Lithium level was way below therapeutic. Anh probably stopped taking her medication which led to this relapse. Dr. Tanaka had been hopeful that Anh would be one of those patients who would stay on her medication, but she knew all too well that stopping bipolar medication when one started feeling better was a common occurrence, especially right after diagnosis. She understood that she herself would likely try to prove the diagnosis wrong by stopping the medication just to see what would happen. This phenomenon occurred so often that she almost expected it as a part of the life cycle of the illness. There was still so much stigma, shame, and misunderstanding surrounding mental illness. Having to put pills into your mouth was a daily reminder of this humiliation, and patients resisted it any way they could.

Dr. Tanaka didn't have any kids of her own. She wondered what it would be like to be a parent, if she would be capable of handling the situations her patients and their parents faced every day. Families came to her with children who tantrummed for hours, children who continued to soil their pants well into their teenage years, children who were depressed, or threatened to kill their entire family, and some who even attempted to do so, starting with their youngest sibling. Families came to her desperate and exhausted, confused by what was going on, but knowing that something was terribly wrong. By the time they found their way to her office, they had already suffered through months, if not years, of sleepless nights and crushing amounts of stress, guilt, shame, exhaustion, and confusion. Sometimes, it would take only a few minutes of her quiet attention before a parent, usually the mother, broke down into tears about how much stress and worry they had been under, and how helpless they felt about the situation.

Lithium was a good medication. It caused side effects, but it worked. But Dr. Tanaka had never personally taken it, so she didn't know what it is like to swallow it down every day. And if she did have her own children, she hoped that they would never have to take it. And yet here she was, about to enter Anh's room to convince her that she needed to get back on it.

When Dr. Tanaka entered Anh's room, she found Anh restlessly pacing back and forth in the small confines of her room like a stymied tiger. There was a hum of frustrated energy emanating from Anh's body. Dr. Tanaka had trained her body to serve as a stethoscope to her patient's internal states. By taking in their facial expression, body language, and their interactions with her, she could sense whether they were calm, angry, sad, or not even in reality. Before she even said a word, Dr. Tanaka knew that Anh was bubbling inside like a volcano about to erupt.

"Get me out of here!!" Anh roared. "Why do you keep locking me up like a prisoner? I need to check on my family and make sure they're OK. There is a huge tsunami coming."

"Your family is safe. They are worried about you and want to make sure that you are OK," Dr. Tanaka replied.

"I'll be much better when you let me out of here!" Anh continued.

"Anh, did you stop taking your Lithium after our last appointment?"

"Of course I did, I don't need that stuff anymore. It just slows me down."

"When did you stop taking it?"

"Does it matter? I stopped it. I don't need it, and I don't want to take it anymore."

"Anh, did you sleep last night?" Dr. Tanaka tried again, trying to find some safe ground to navigate around this smoldering cinder cone.

"I can't sleep on these beds, they're so uncomfortable. Let me go home."

"I want you to go home too, but first, we need to make sure you're sleeping better and thinking clearly," Dr. Tanaka explained. She knew that further conversation would not be helpful. Anh was not in a state to be reasoned with.

"I'm as clear as a bell. You're the one who needs to put her glasses on." Without warning, Anh lunged at Dr. Tanaka as if she was going to tackle her.

Dr. Tanaka had left the door open for this very reason. She learned early on in her residency to always be ready in case of patient assaults. On instinct, she quickly backed out of the doorway and yelled "STAFF!" which was the unit code for all staff to rush to her assistance. In a flash, several staff members grabbed Anh and restrained her to the floor. Anh continued to squirm and resist. The more they restrained her, the more she fought back, screaming at the top of her lungs, "Let me go, you're hurting me!"

The unit nurse asked, "Doc, do you want to give her any meds?"

Dr. Tanaka did not like forcing treatment on anyone, much less a minor, but Anh was clearly agitated, and a potential danger to herself and others. "Ask her if she'll take some oral Haldol. If not, give her a shot." This was a part of her job that Dr. Tanaka did not enjoy.

Chapter 19 - Xuan

1992

I stand on the shores of Ala Moana Beach, looking out on the water. It is close to sunset. The canoe paddlers are making their way into shore, their sleek vessels slicing cleanly through the glistening golden water. Children are playing in the shallow waters, splashing each other and giggling in delight. I remember when Anh and Jack were young, and Long and I would take them to have barbecue picnics at the beach. The children were always impatient for Long to finish blowing up their rainbow-colored swim-rings for them. I don't know how to swim, so I am fearful of the water, even as beautiful as it is. Even though it looks calm and peaceful at times, I worry if the waves get too rough. I have to watch the kids closely at all times, so they don't get hurt in the water.

When I look out at the ocean, I imagine my ancestors looking back at me across the Pacific Ocean from the shores of Vietnam. I can feel the sadness in the water, and the sorrow in my heart. I wonder if I will ever see Vietnam again, my motherland, the place where I was born and raised. Our family was lucky to be able to leave Vietnam safely, but I didn't even have a chance to say goodbye. I think about the thousands of my fellow countrymen and women who died as boat people trying to leave Vietnam, how their bodies were lost in the waves of the Pacific Ocean as they tried to escape war and poverty to find a new home to establish their lives. The dark waters of the ocean still hold their pain, their trauma, their tears, the stories of their unlived lives echoing like ghosts underwater. And the ones who survived, like me, are now living out our own broken lives on land, trying to piece together a new story that never feels quite whole or complete. There are always gaps and cracks, but I don't know what to fill them with. What is happening to my daughter Anh? Is our family being punished for leaving our ancestors behind in Vietnam? Is this bad karma from a past life?

There is a deep ache in my heart for what the war did to my country and family. I feel this heaviness in my chest that never goes away. I think about those who stayed behind in Vietnam after the war ended, those who had no choice. I wonder what life is like for them on the other side of the Pacific. I feel guilty for the safety and comfort I enjoy here in the paradise of Hawaii. Would my life, and the lives of those who stayed behind, ever cross paths again? Would we be able to find some common ground across this big ocean? Or would all our shattered lives, hopes, and dreams remain afloat or sunken in that big blue body of water between us, with no shared shore for us to hug and comfort one another's tears?

I walk along the sandy beach, listening to the rhythmic sound of the ocean lapping back and forth, in and out from the shore. I am grateful for finding refuge in Hawaii after the war. The land here is so beautiful, the weather mild, and the people friendly. It is not easy to be a refugee anywhere, but to be a refugee who washes up on the shores of Hawaii is like winning the refugee lottery. There are a lot of Asian people in Hawaii so there is less discrimination here against us. I often hear stories about Vietnamese refugees who settle on the mainland, who live in snow, who are discriminated against or looked down on at work, or their children bullied at school. Hawaii took in my family with welcome arms and protected us from the storms of violence and poverty of our own country. But now something is attacking my daughter Anh from the inside, and I have no idea how to defend Anh from this attack.

My mother taught me that everyone has a fate and a destiny, and if we live our lives well, our destiny will lead us to a better place than where we started. Anh's illness is happening for a reason. There is a lesson or karma here for us to learn from. But what is it? What am I supposed to do? What can I do to make Anh better? I pray to Buddha, to

Phật Bà Quán Thế Âm Bồ Tát, the Buddha of Compassion, for support. I will do whatever Buddha wants me to do, as long as Anh gets better.

I miss Vietnam terribly. I miss the places and memories from my childhood – the smell of Bà Binh's *phở* shop, the warm, humid wind blowing off the river on my cheek, and the familiar routine of coming home and sharing a meal with my parents. I miss having *phở* for breakfast. I can never understand how the American custom of cold milk and cereal nourishes one's empty belly in the morning. In fact, it feels more like a rude awakening. I miss the comfort of a warm soothing bowl of noodle soup with its soft, slippery noodles and tender pieces of thin beef and the aromatic smell of green onions and cilantro. The first warm swallow of rich broth awakens not only the Vietnamese belly but the Vietnamese soul.

I am sad that my children do not know their beautiful motherland, the roots of their Vietnamese people and heritage. They are Vietnamese who have never set foot on Vietnamese soil. What will they know of Vietnam besides what I share with them, my own fading and troubled memories? I feel torn between keeping them Vietnamese and allowing them to become American. What will be better for them? What is my duty and responsibility as their mother, the link between their past and their future, the old and the new, Vietnam and America, war and peace? I have no answers, and the questions themselves make me so confused that I block them out of my mind and focus on what I need to get through each day. Sometimes I feel so lost, like I have been tumbled in the waves and cannot tell which way is up or down, forward or backward. All I can count on is getting up each morning and going to work to make enough money to make sure that my family is fed and the kids go to school. I have Long, but I feel so lonely navigating this voyage. We did not come to Hawaii as boat people, but living and raising our children in America feels like living on a floating raft in an open sea with no roots or direction to guide us home.

Chapter 20 - Anh

1992

"Hey, you, you're new," a girl with dirty-blond hair says in my direction as the adolescents on the unit start to gather for morning group in the community room.

The last time I was here, I didn't speak to any of the other kids on the unit, and that's my plan for this hospitalization as well.

"How many times have you been here? I haven't seen you before. This is my tenth time here," the girl goes on. I can't tell if she is bragging about being admitted to Kahi ten times or not.

"This is my second time here," I reply, wondering how I can break off this conversation without appearing rude. Being on a locked unit with 12 other adolescents, it's best not to rub anyone the wrong way. I briefly glance up at the girl and can't help noticing the myriad of crisscrossed scars and lines on her forearms. "What happened?" I blurt out.

The girl follows my gaze to her bare arms. "Oh, these things? I did them, of course. Nothing this time, but these..." she went on nonchalantly, pointing at some of the lines that looked more recent than some of the other scars, "...these are from a few weeks ago when my boyfriend broke up with me. That bastard, he was cheating on me with another girl. He doesn't even deserve these scars."

"Does it hurt?" I ask, still confused about what exactly she meant when she said she'd done them.

"Of course it hurts, stupid, that's the whole point. To show the world how much you're hurting on the inside on the outside," she laughs back.

I am quiet. I don't like being called stupid. This girl seems like she belongs here at Kahi. I feel like I'm being wrongly punished for a crime I didn't commit.

"Don't look so shocked, Asian girl. You've never cut before? I'll teach you how if you're curious. I've done it with everything you can think of – pens, pencils, razors, knives, keys, anything sharp."

"Uh, no thanks," I reply.

"What, is your pure skin too good for this?" the girl taunts. "What school you go to?"

I hesitate. I do not like telling other people I go to Punahou. I assume they'll think I'm a rich spoiled brat. I don't have to answer her.

"You look like the type that goes to Punahou," the girl spits out. "Am I right?"

I don't know how to respond, but end up nodding my head slightly, almost in embarrassment.

"I knew it. I know your type. I go to Roosevelt, that public school down the street from you guys, you ever heard of it?"

I nod dumbly again. I feel as if this girl isn't interested in actually having a conversation, but more interested in having someone listen to her.

"Well, Roosevelt's where all you guys go when you get kicked out of your fancy private school after you screw up. Send them to Roosevelt, where everyone is welcome," she goes on sarcastically. "Everyone except for me, of course. Imagine that! They're trying to kick me out of Roosevelt because I keep getting hospitalized all the time. The principal, Mr. Brewer said, 'Shelly doesn't seem to be a good fit for our educational program here due to all the time she has missed. I recommend she try independent study.' Independent study, that's code for, 'We've given up on you, don't even bother to come to campus anymore. Do what you want with your own life,' *independently*, of course."

"Alright, group, let's get started," the group leader on the unit calls to everyone. "Today is Tuesday. Let's go around and say your name and what your goal is today...."

I am relieved for the interruption.

"Hey, Punahou, want to be my partner?" Shelly asks me after the group leader asks the group to pair off for an exercise.

"That's not my name," I answer.

"So why don't you tell me your name then?"

"It's Anh."

"OK, Anh. Will you be my partner?" Shelly asks, getting down on one knee in a dramatic flourish as if she is making a wedding proposal.

I can't help but laugh. "Alright."

The group leader instructs us that this is an exercise on listening. We will take turns listening to one another talk about ourselves for five minutes, without interrupting or jumping in with advice or questions.

"You go first, Anh. I talked too much already." Shelly says.

I panic. I don't know what to say. I'm not used to talking about myself in front of others. I sit there silently for a while. I can see Shelly biting back her lip, trying her best not to jump in with her own thoughts. She finally can't help herself from blurting out a few words, "Just start, anywhere," and then quickly covers up her mouth in mock embarrassment.

"OK, well, I have a younger brother who is 13. My parents are from Vietnam. They own a tourist shop in Waikiki, and I work there on the weekends and during the summer. I play the piano and I like to paint watercolors. My favorite Vietnamese food is *chả giò* or spring rolls. My favorite American food is combination pizza. I want to learn how to surf, but my parents say it's too dangerous." I am surprised at how easy it is to keep on going when no one interrupts me. I usually try to deflect attention and conversation away from myself. But this is a new experience for me – to talk about myself without interruption or comment. I don't think anyone has ever asked me to do that before. The five minutes go by faster than I expect. I can tell that Shelly is genuinely listening and isn't working at keeping quiet anymore.

"Time's up," the group leader announces. "Switch roles now and have the other person talk about themselves for five minutes. Remember, if you're the listener, no talking or interrupting. Just listen."

Shelly responds, "Wow, that was pretty interesting. I've never met a Vietnamese person before. I don't think I even know where Vietnam is. My family has been in Hawaii for a long time. Or at least that's what my mom tells me. I don't know my dad. I've never met him. My mom said his name was Mac and that he was out of our lives quicker than you could eat a Big Mac. He was haole, that's where I got my green eyes from. My mom and her family say that the haoles stole our land from us, and that's why we are homeless and have to camp on the beach. But I don't mind. I like camping at the beach. It's better than those dirty apartments we used to stay at where there were huge flying cockroaches everywhere. That was when my mom's boyfriend Keoni lived with us. She and Keoni broke up last year, and since then, we haven't found a place to live yet. My mom's trying to find a job, but she says that people discriminate against her. She applied at McDonald's and Burger King, but even they wouldn't give her a job. She says that the Asian store managers are the worst. They only hire people who look like them."

I am glad I don't have to respond to that comment. I wouldn't know what to say. When my parents are looking to hire a new employee for our store, I remember them saying that they preferred hiring someone Asian. For some reason, they feel like they can trust fair-skinned Asian women the most. My mother even told me, "I don't trust those haole workers. Cô Thanh tells me that they try and shoplift from her all the time."

Shelly goes on with her story. "I'm supposed to be a junior. But like I told you earlier, Roosevelt is trying to kick me out. I've changed schools so many times that I don't think I've ever actually finished a class at one school. But I don't care. School's a joke anyway. How's a piece of paper going to help you survive in life? I can't wait until I turn 18 so I can leave this island and never come back."

I wonder if that means that Shelly will never come back to see her family again. I also have plans to go to the mainland for college after graduating high school, but I have never imagined leaving for good. I don't know what it would feel like to leave a place for good and never go back.

"Alright, time's up, everyone. How was that experience for everyone?" the group leader asks the group.

Shelly and I look at each other and simultaneously say, "Interesting."

Chapter 21- Anh

1992

This time when I return to school, I can't face anyone – my teachers, classmates, or even my friends. At lunchtime, I run to the girls' locker room bathroom, the one that's hidden away from everyone. I lock the door behind me and sit down on the toilet seat with my pants still on. I don't come here to use the bathroom. I come here to be alone, to be left alone, to hide my shame and loneliness from everyone. I do not want to talk to anyone. I pull out my brown paper bag with my turkey sandwich wrapped in plastic wrap. But I have no appetite. This is depressing, sitting here in a bathroom stall with my lunch. How low can I go? I hear the bathroom door swing open and several girls come in. They are chatting happily about their weekend plans and where they will go and whose house they will meet at. Their innocent laughter makes me feel even worse. I feel like we inhabit completely different worlds, two worlds that will never intersect. The girls flush, wash their hands and leave the bathroom, continuing on with their chatter. I am left behind alone.

I think about Shelly, whom I got to know during my last hospitalization. This time I only stayed a week, but we spent a lot of time together. Being locked up in a small hospital ward 24/7 left a lot of downtime to fill. After we were partners for that listening exercise, we started eating our meals together and talking more. Shelly left the hospital before me, but we exchanged phone numbers so we could call each other on the outside.

Shelly is different from my Punahou friends. I have never met someone who is homeless before, someone who camps on the beach, and someone who cuts on her arms and legs on a regular basis. But in a way, I feel like I have more in common with Shelly than some of my Punahou classmates who don't know what it's like to be locked up in a psychiatric hospital and be forced to take medication that supposedly will restore you to the land of the sane.

In the hospital, Shelly and I both had Dr. Tanaka as our psychiatrist. Shelly told me that the doctor was giving her a medication named Prozac to help with her depression and anxiety. She didn't like taking it and vowed to stop taking it as soon as they let her out of the hospital. "All these adults think they know what's best for us. Well, they don't. You only have yourself to count on and trust," Shelly told me.

I hear Bà nội reciting her Buddhist prayers, *Nam Mô A Di Đà Phật. Nam Mô A Di Đà Phật.* Bà nội is wearing her plain brown prayer robes. In her hands, she is holding a chain of Buddhist beads and slowly rolling her fingers over the 108 circular beads on the strand, reciting the same prayer with each bead. Bà nội has taught me several of these prayers, addressing the names of the different Buddhist gods. Each one has a particular area of protection. She teaches me to pray to *Phật Bà Quán Thế Âm Bồ Tát* in times of danger when I am scared for my safety, and to pray to *Phật Dược Sư Lưu Ly* when I am sick. Sometimes Bà nội asks me to sit down with her to recite the prayers, but I often get bored chanting words I don't understand. And my butt gets numb from sitting in one position too long. But I like listening to my grandmother chant. Prayer is very important to Bà nội. It's her way of connecting with the ancestors and the spirit world, to ask for blessings and protection in the physical realm. Bà nội teaches me that doing my prayers and tending to the altar honors my ancestors. "If you don't remember your roots and connection to the past, how can you expect to live the right way and make decisions in your life for the future? Forgetting your past is like forgetting all the lessons you should have already learned. You can't move forward in your karma if you keep making the same mistakes from your past and ignore the lessons that your parents and ancestors are teaching you," Bà nội says to me.

Listen to your parents and elders. This is a mantra I have heard my whole life, maybe even from inside the womb. I'm not sure if I believe in past lives and karma. Part of it makes sense, but part of it also makes no sense, and I wonder if it isn't some Vietnamese parenting trick to get children to listen to our elders without question. At times I feel like what my parents tell me to do is exactly the opposite of what I believe will make me happy.

My parents tell me that girls should not play sports because they are dangerous. They tell me that studying and my education are the most important things for me to focus on, that family is more important than friends. My grandmother and mother tell me to always back down in a fight, especially with my brother, because Vietnamese women should be soft and forgiving because they are the more flexible of the two sexes. My mother tells me to be patient, that water eventually wears down stone because being fluid allows one to adapt to circumstances, and over time, water will always cut a path to the ocean. Rocks can't move, they can only be shaped by the path of the water.

What are my ancestors trying to teach me? What lessons am I supposed to be learning right now? I hear myself murmuring *Nam Mô Đại Bi Quán Thế Âm Bồ Tát* over and over again.

I am a Chinese acrobatic dancer. I wear a beautiful red silk dress with long colorful silk ribbons that flutter behind. I perform a visually stunning dance with several other dancers. We balance large and extremely heavy blue and white porcelain vases on our heads while maneuvering gracefully through complex jumps and leaps. It takes an extreme amount of effort and concentration to keep the vases balanced on our heads. At some point, my body can no longer keep dancing and hold up the heavy vase at the same time. I feel the vase slipping off my head and it falls to the ground and shatters into thousands of tiny pieces.

I wake up from my dream just as the vase smashes to the ground with a loud crash. My heart is still pounding from the shock of having dropped the precious object. But as I lie there in bed, replaying in slow motion the moment that the vase hit the ground and shattered to pieces, I feel that the vase that I was trying so hard to balance on my head while dancing beautifully is a metaphor for the burden of having to hold myself together with the illusion of control and perfection. Sometimes things need to be broken before they can become whole again.

Chapter 22- Xuan

1992

I cannot help thinking about my uncle in Vietnam, the one who killed himself when I was only five years old. No one in my family ever talks about him, but I remember the day my mother and I walked out into our yard and found him hanging from a thick branch of our mango tree. His neck was cocked at a crooked angle, and I wondered why he was hanging up there like that. My mother howled a sound I had never heard before. My father ran into the yard from the house and grabbed my uncle's swaying legs. My aunt pulled me away into the house. I hadn't understood what had happened, and no one ever explained it to me. As I grew older, I came to the frightening conclusion that my uncle had committed suicide, but I didn't dare ask my parents about it. I was sure they would ignore me or slap my face in anger for bringing up the topic that we couldn't talk about. But that didn't make me stop thinking about it all the time privately. Why did my uncle want to kill himself?

I have heard people say that people who kill themselves are "crazy in the head." Was my uncle "crazy in the head?" Is my daughter now "crazy in the head?" Would Anh try to kill herself? I cannot bring myself to utter those words out loud to Long. I never imagined that my daughter would have a mental illness. I did not even know what a mental illness was before Anh went to the hospital. Bipolar disorder is what Dr. Tanaka keeps saying is the name of the disease Anh has. It is not a term I am familiar with, nor do I know of its equivalent in Vietnamese. In Vietnam, people with mental problems are just labeled "*khung*" or "crazy." There is no distinction between different kinds or degrees of "*khung.*" You either are crazy or not. So it is difficult for me to understand what Dr. Tanaka means when she tells us that Anh has bipolar disorder, but that it does not mean that she is crazy or abnormal, and that if Anh takes her medication, she can have a normal life.

Raising a child is a difficult task, but I grew up watching my own mother and aunts taking care of groups of children in our neighborhood. I understand those tasks of caring for a child – they have to be fed, and need clean clothes to wear, and lessons about the importance of their education and listening to their elders. Taking care of a child with a mental illness in America is something I do not know how to do. I feel so completely lost. I don't know what the right answer is. I feel powerless over the illness, powerless over the medication, powerless over the outcome. Will Anh ever get better? What does her future hold? Can Anh still achieve the dreams Long and I had for her? All the crazy people I knew in Vietnam ended up with pitiful lives wandering the streets, begging, or forever burdening their families with their care.

What makes it even more difficult for me is how Anh's illness is hidden from the outside. She doesn't have a broken bone or fever that I can watch heal. I can't see or understand what is going on inside her mind. I sometimes wonder if Anh is just misbehaving and acting like this to cause Long and me to suffer. But I know that is not true. I know our daughter is suffering greatly and would not make up something like this. Sometimes when I look at Anh, I can catch a glimpse of how crushed she is by her illness. When my friends at temple ask how the children are doing, I cannot bring myself to tell them about Anh's illness. I fear my friends will blame me as a mother, or our family for causing her illness. Worse, they will start talking about it to their friends, and soon everyone will think that our family is crazy. I don't tell my friends about the sleepless nights I lie awake in my bed, filled with anxiety about Anh's future. I don't share with them that Anh is taking powerful Western medication that is making her fat. I don't tell them that sometimes I feel like I am losing my own mind and don't know if I will be strong enough to get through this.

I wonder if Anh's illness is my bad karma. I wonder what I have done in my past lives to deserve this punishment and whether Buddha will give me the strength to bear it out. Sometimes I think about closing my eyes and never waking up, drifting away, surrendering to the nightmare that has become our family's life. Long and I barely speak to each other anymore, we don't know what to say. I get up each morning, get dressed, and go to work, my body going through the motions as if I'm already a ghost. My mind is always elsewhere, as if my thoughts have been shoplifted by an unknown thief and locked into a dungeon with the key thrown away. I feel trapped by my situation. I can find no hope in the darkness. I can find nothing to hold onto, no light to guide my way, unsure if there is even an exit to this dark tunnel. I feel my own self slipping away. I don't know if I can continue to do this. But I have to keep on going. I am the mother, I cannot give up. What will Anh do if I give up? Who will be strong for Anh?

Chapter 23- Dr. Tanaka

1992

When Dr. Tanaka saw Anh and her parents back in her office again for a follow-up after her most recent hospitalization, something had shifted. She couldn't identify exactly what it was yet, but it was significant.

Anh looked more forlorn and vulnerable than before. Dr. Tanaka recognized that look of helplessness when someone no longer even had the strength to fight back. And as Dr. Tanaka sat there with Anh, she felt a wave of love and tenderness towards this young girl in front of her. She imagined Anh being a young baby who needed to be swaddled up in a blanket and comforted.

Dr. Tanaka saw most of her patients for medication only. But she did have a handful of therapy clients whom she saw more frequently. She enjoyed the intimacy of therapy, of really getting to know someone, and the trust they built in each other during this challenging time in their lives. The familiarity she built with a patient, meeting week after week with them, was different from the relationship she had with her patients she saw once a month to adjust their medication.

"I'm sorry that Anh had to be hospitalized again. I recommend that Anh give therapy a try. It might help her feel more supported through this difficult experience," Dr. Tanaka suggested. Anh and her parents had declined her recommendation for therapy after Anh's first hospitalization. The family felt that medication was enough and did not see the need for therapy. She wasn't sure they even knew what she meant by therapy. Many people question how talking about an illness can make it better.

Dr. Tanaka felt a pull to take on Anh as a therapy client. There was something about the teenager that she felt connected to even from their first meeting.

"Maybe if I saw Anh more often to start with, then your family can see how the therapy goes?" Dr. Tanaka offered.

"How often do you want to see Anh?" Long asked.

"Well, I'm seeing her once a month right now, so maybe we could try every two weeks to start with?"

"Every two weeks?" Xuan exclaimed in a panic. "She must be very sick for you to have to check up on her so often."

"No, seeing her more frequently doesn't mean she is more sick. It just means that I want to support her more during this difficult time." Dr. Tanaka looked at Anh to see if she could get a sense of how Anh was taking in this exchange. But Anh continued to look dejected and hopeless, as if she was used to her parents making decisions for her.

"Will we have to pay more for this?" Long asked.

"No, your insurance will cover the therapy. And it will help me monitor Anh's medication closer as well. What do you think, Anh?"

Anh and Dr. Tanaka made eye contact with one another, and in that gaze, Dr. Tanaka saw a flicker of hope light up, and Anh nodded in assent.

The next time Anh had an appointment with Dr. Tanaka, the doctor told her parents that she would like to spend the entire session time alone with Anh. When Dr. Tanaka came out to the waiting area to call Anh in for her appointment, she noticed how anxious Anh appeared.

It can be anxiety-provoking to start a therapy relationship, for both the patient and the therapist. It is like going on a date with someone and trying to figure out how it will go for the next hour or so. For herself, she knew what a commitment therapy was, and what it would entail for it to be successful. A patient had to be willing to be vulnerable, have the courage to truly open up and be seen, to show those parts of themselves that they often tried their best to hide, even to themselves, often due to shame and guilt. As a therapist, it would take a large amount of patience, and faith, that her consistent efforts, good intentions, and genuine love and care for her patients, would be enough to help them find their way. But for now, they were just beginning.

"How are you today?" Dr. Tanaka asked.

"OK," Anh replied, still looking uncomfortable.

"How was school?" Dr. Tanaka offered another non-threatening opener.

"OK."

Dr. Tanaka sat there for a moment and smiled at Anh in silence, trying to calm the anxiety in the room. When no one broke the silence, and the tension was as thick as ever, Dr. Tanaka decided to name it. "I bet it feels pretty awkward and uncomfortable sitting here staring at each other, doesn't it?"

Anh couldn't help but crack a small smile and chuckle, "Yeah."

"Well, it's pretty normal to feel anxious starting out. But I hope you'll feel more comfortable as time goes on and we get to know each other better."

Anh nodded slightly.

Dr. Tanaka continued on. She learned that when working with kids and teenagers, sometimes you have to show them how to use words to express themselves. The abstinent silence of her adult therapy training was usually not helpful with the younger age groups who were already naturally less defended than adults. Children are quick to mirror who they are around. If she could act comfortable and real around them, then they were more likely to do the same with her.

"I can't imagine what the past few months have been like for you." Dr. Tanaka chose her words carefully. Even though she had worked with hundreds of children and their families through similar first-break episodes, hospitalizations, and relapses, and had even worked on the psychiatric wards herself, she knew that she had never been locked up and held against her will, forced to take medication, or been a parent of a child undergoing that experience. As much as she wanted to convey empathy and understanding of her patients' experiences, she knew that there would always be a gulf between their experiences and her understanding of them. But she wanted her patients to know how much she truly wanted to understand their experience, and to help them feel loved and supported through it.

"It sucks. My life is ruined. I can't ever get it back again," the words came out of Anh's mouth in a surprising gush.

Dr. Tanaka waited to see if there was anything else Anh wanted to add. She had learned that sometimes pausing was more fruitful than rushing to fill in the quiet spaces.

When Anh didn't say anything further, Dr. Tanaka prompted again, "What's been the hardest part?"

"I don't know, just the feeling that everything has changed, and that nothing will ever be the same again."

Dr. Tanaka was impressed by the insight in Anh's response, a recognition of the significance of her recent diagnosis and hospitalizations. "And that's scary," she offered.

Anh nodded in agreement. "I'm scared that I'll never be normal, that I'll never get better, that I'll have to take this awful medication forever."

"Those are big things to be scared about. But I've seen you be very brave through all this."

"It's just an act. I'm not brave at all," Anh countered.

"Being brave doesn't always mean you feel brave."

"What do you mean? Doesn't being brave mean not getting scared?"

"My definition of being brave is that you might feel scared, but you have the courage to keep going anyways." Dr. Tanaka offered.

"Well, it's not like I've really had a choice in all of this," Anh replied, again downplaying her own strength.

"You're here today, and that's something."

"Not much. My parents don't know, but I skipped my afternoon classes today before coming to see you," Anh admitted, half-worried that she would get in trouble.

"How come?"

"I just wasn't feeling good. I ate lunch in the bathroom by myself and couldn't face going back to class after that," her face looked ashamed that she had let anyone know how low she had sunk.

Dr. Tanaka didn't react with shock or judgment and instead surprised Anh with a compliment.

"So it took a lot for you to come in and see me today."

"Like I said, I didn't have a choice. My parents were expecting to pick me up and take me here for our appointment."

"You don't give yourself much credit, do you?" Dr. Tanaka observed playfully. She noted that her efforts to praise Anh were frequently met with minimization. She wondered how much of this was cultural, or a reflection of Anh's self-esteem, or whether the two could even be separated. Asian parents, including her own, often drilled into their children the importance of humility, and not accepting praise for fear of being seen as arrogant.

Anh didn't respond to Dr. Tanaka's last comment. It looked like Anh might have taken her playful comment as another criticism of herself. Dr. Tanaka made a mental note to be more careful about humor until they knew each other better.

"Thank you for showing up today. I look forward to seeing you the next time," Dr. Tanaka said at the end of their session.

Anh didn't say anything as she stood up and walked out the door.

Chapter 24 - Anh

1992

"How was your appointment with the doctor?" my mom asks me as soon as I walk into the lobby.

"I don't feel like talking about it," I reply.

"What did you two talk about?" my mom continues to press on, as if she didn't hear my response.

"I said I don't want to talk about it." I can feel the familiar irritation rising in my voice.

"Why are you so angry? I only ask because I worry about you," my mother continues, which only makes me more irritated. I try to ignore my mother's usual pattern of nosy prodding, anxiety, and then self-righteous indignation. "You children are so disrespectful. If I'm talking to you, you must answer my questions. America has made you all spoiled." And then she proceeds to launch into the familiar refrains of how America has corrupted our family, punctuated by pleas to the universe to tell her what she has done in her past lives to deserve this suffering.

I usually start tuning my mom out when she gets like this. There is no possibility of having a rational conversation with her that will end well. I have a complicated relationship with my parents. For the most part, I know that even though they aren't perfect, they aren't the worse parents either. They work hard and provide our family with a home, food, and education. They sometimes get angry and yell at me, especially my dad, but they don't hit or abuse me.

But there is always a distance between us that I can't clearly describe. I see how some of my friends and their parents interact with each other, and it is so different from my relationship with my parents. With us, there is no joking around or casual banter. Even when I try to bring up a serious question for discussion with them, it is usually met with a curt response that does not allow further conversation. I know what I can and what I can't talk to my parents about. I can ask them for money to pay for something I need for school or want from the mall. I can ask them to sign my permission slips and forms for school. But anything else that's personal, or that I need help with, I either take care of it myself or find someone else to help me.

I remember when I had a hard time adjusting to Punahou in sixth grade, I tried telling my mom about it. "Mom, I don't know anybody at my new school. I want to go back to my old school."

"Of course you don't know anyone there. You're new. You can't go back to your old school. This is a better school."

"But I don't have any friends to eat lunch with, and there are no other new kids in my class. Everyone already has their friends."

"Your studies are more important than friends. Focus on your schoolwork."

It was useless to try and get my mom to understand. But that didn't help with the loneliness I felt at school. Over time I got used to that loneliness as a part of myself. I did eventually make some friends, but there was always a lingering feeling that I didn't belong there, that I was an outsider trying to gain admission to something that had started way before I even knew about it.

I get into a routine of coming to Dr. Tanaka's office every Tuesday afternoon after school. I check in for my appointment and then wait in the sparse lobby until Dr. Tanaka comes out to get me at exactly 4 pm. Dr. Tanaka always comes out of her office right on the dot at 4 o'clock, and I wonder whether she is sitting in her office watching the second hand on her watch strike 4 o'clock exactly before coming out to get me.

We both settle into our seats. "How are you today, Anh?" Dr. Tanaka always asks to start our appointment.

"OK," I reply, even though I don't feel that good.

"How was school?" Dr. Tanaka starts again. I have gotten used to how our conversations begin.

"Today was hard. I felt kinda blah. I didn't want to be there."

"Was there anything in particular that made today hard?"

"No, it was just a normal school day. I just didn't feel normal."

"How did you feel?"

"I don't know. It's hard to describe. I just felt yucky all day."

"What does yucky feel like to you?"

Dr. Tanaka usually responds to my responses with another question. At first, it annoyed me, but now I realize that she is trying to help me get better at describing what I'm feeling.

"It feels like a heaviness, like something weighing down on my chest and throat. It makes me not want to talk to anyone. I can't even force a smile or pretend like everything's OK."

"It's hard pretending to feel something you're not." Dr. Tanaka agrees.

"But I used to be able to," I reply. "I used to be able to just pretend I was OK, and no one could tell how I was really feeling. Now it's so bad that I can't hide it anymore."

"Maybe it's a good thing that you're not hiding it anymore."

"How can it be a good thing to have other people look at you and see that you have mental problems?!" I exclaim in disbelief. "I look at other kids at my school, and they're all walking around smiling, laughing, and joking about stupid stuff, and I feel like I'm on a different planet than them. I'm in my little own depressed world that feels like shit. I want to be normal just like everyone else, but I'm not. I can't even pretend to be like them now. There's this wall between us. I've entered a new world and I can never go back to the world they live in anymore."

"That must be really hard for you," Dr. Tanaka says with an empathic expression on her face. "Are you able to talk to any of your friends about this?"

"Not really. I have one friend Lauren who I shared some stuff with when I got out of the hospital the first time, but not so much anymore.

There's only so much someone can listen to about your mental problems. It's not exactly a fun topic."

"Do you know anyone else at your school who might also be going through similar experiences?"

"Hell no, or at least no one has shared it with me. I met another girl in the hospital the last time I was there, though. It did feel good to talk to someone else going through similar stuff."

"I'm glad you talked to someone else in the hospital. It's helpful to know that you're not the only one feeling this way. It's important for you to know that a lot of other kids at your school are probably having emotional difficulties too. We have an adolescent group here at the clinic once a week if you're interested." Dr. Tanaka offers.

"No, thank you," I reply right away. "I don't feel like meeting other crazy teenagers and having them know all my problems."

"Most of them end up really liking it."

"No, I'm not interested. Plus I already come to see you once a week. If I did the group, then I would have to come here twice a week? That's a lot."

"Yes, it is a lot. Therapy is really hard work, and I'm proud of you for coming in here every week to see me. It's not easy being honest with yourself, much less sharing with someone else how you're really feeling. Being a teenager is hard enough. Being a teenager dealing with mental health issues is a whole other ballgame."

"Why do I have to go through this? Why can't I just be like other kids?"

"That's a question that's hard to answer. Why any particular person ends up having depression, anxiety, bipolar disorder, or schizophrenia is the result of many factors. But we do know that biology and genetics have a lot to do with it. So partly it's just about what genes you were born with."

"You mean it's hereditary? Like my parents passed this down to me?"

"Partly, yes. But genes are complicated. Your parents definitely gave you their genetic material, but then there are so many factors that play into whether those genes are expressed or not."

"You mean I could have prevented this from happening?" I ask.

"No, that's not what I meant. You and your parents could not have prevented this from happening, and it's not anyone's fault. It's just hard to point to one thing as the reason for it."

"Well, that's just my luck then," I sigh.

"You didn't have any control over your manic episodes. But now that you're in treatment and taking care of it, you're doing everything you can to manage it, and that's laudable. Some families don't come into treatment even though they are suffering."

"What does 'laudable' mean?" I ask.

"It means something deserving praise. Something to be proud of."

"Well, it's not like I have a choice about it. My parents make me come every week, and they make me take my medication."

"It may not feel like you have a choice. But you do, and you're making good choices. You could refuse to take the medication, or refuse to come here, or come here and refuse to talk to me. But you're not doing any of those things. You're choosing to trust in this process of getting better."

"I don't know if I actually trust it. I just don't have the energy to fight it," I reply as I feel a wave of exhaustion wash over me. "I'm so tired of all this."

"Well, I'm glad you're not fighting it. And I hope I can earn your trust so that you can let me help you through this. All of this is too much for one person or one family to carry on their own. I'm here to help you and your family through this."

I don't respond verbally, but I nod my head ever so slightly. It is time for our session to end.

Chapter 25 - Xuan

1993

I feel a deep heaviness in my chest and body ever since Anh has gotten sick. Maybe it has always been there, and now I am just noticing it. It feels like an overwhelming sadness. There has been so much sadness in my life that I have stuffed away somewhere deep inside myself. Otherwise, it is too overwhelming and too heavy to carry around on the surface and be able to function on a daily basis. When I was a teenager, my father told me that our country Vietnam had always been at war, for thousands of years. Whether it was the Chinese, the French, the Japanese, the Americans, or even other Vietnamese, the soil of our land has been constantly watered by blood and tears. I can't help but believe that a river of sorrow is born into every Vietnamese family as a part of our cultural inheritance. I had hoped that being born in America would spare my children some of this sorrow. It appears that crossing the ocean has spared our family some bloodshed, but not our share of Vietnamese sorrow that is a part of our country's inheritance. In Vietnamese, the word for water is nước. In Vietnamese, the word for country is also nước. In the same way our children are born through our waters, we Vietnamese are born from our motherland. Water gives us life, and our motherland also gives us life. Losing our country has been like losing a mother, and this sorrow lives on in our bodies. But water does not have a country, water belongs everywhere, to everyone. Water connects Vietnam to Hawaii, my past and my present.

Ever since Anh has gotten sick, I feel like I am falling backwards into this land of pain and sorrow, a land of war and bloodshed that has torn

Vietnamese families apart for centuries. It is a bottomless ocean of pain and tears. I cry endlessly each night and am shocked that my body can reproduce the same voluminous outpouring of tears the next day. The source of my pain and tears seems infinite, stretching all the way back across the ocean to Vietnam. I cry for my daughter. I cry for her unborn children. I cry for our family, for our deceased ancestors, for the ghosts that still haunt our motherland.

Dr. Tanaka has asked Long and me to come in for an appointment to check in with her. "Why does the doctor want to see us?" Long asks me nervously as we sit in the lobby. "Is there anything wrong?"

"I don't know either," I reply. "She just told me when I picked Anh up yesterday that she wanted to speak with us today."

Dr. Tanaka walks out into the waiting area to gesture us back to her office.

"Thank you for coming in today. How do you both feel Anh is doing?" Dr. Tanaka asks us.

"Good, she is doing good," Long replies for both of us.

"Any problems with the medication?"

"No, no problem at all," Long answers congenially.

"How long will Anh have to take it?" I ask impulsively. I see the doctor hesitate before answering.

"I like to see patients stay on their medication and do well for at least one year before we decide what to do next. I agree that Anh is doing much better, and her weight gain on the Lithium has stabilized, so I recommend she continue taking it for now."

"Will she have to take it for the rest of her life?" I ask again, desperate to know when this illness will end.

"I don't have the answer to that right now. Some people are able to get off their medication, and some people's symptoms return when they stop their medication, so it's different for everyone, and we'll just have to wait and see," the doctor says. She went on, "Your family has done very well in treatment. We got a hold of this early, and you both have been so good at keeping up with her medication and therapy appointments. You really are doing everything you can to help her."

Long and I nod uncomfortably. Why is this doctor telling us that we are doing a good job when our daughter is still sick? It doesn't make any sense.

"How are you both doing?" the doctor asks us.

I do not understand what the doctor is trying to ask, what the correct answer to this question is. I want to cry and tell the doctor that it has been so difficult, but no words come out of my mouth.

"Sometimes it is very difficult for parents as well to deal with all this," the doctor says again. Long and I continue to sit in silence.

"Well, thank you for coming in today. Do you have any other questions or concerns you want to talk about?"

We both shake our heads and leave the appointment.

Chapter 26 - Anh

1993

It has been a long time since I picked up a paintbrush. It's one of those things that slipped out of my routine. But today, sitting at home, I find myself bored. I turn on the TV and flip the channels through the usual weekday afternoon mix of trashy talk shows, cartoons, and infomercials selling juicers and home fitness systems. I turn off the TV and put on my headphones instead and try listening to CDs. But I find myself repeatedly pushing the skip button because the sounds coming into my ears do not match the soundtrack I am feeling inside.

Restless and tired, I look around the room when my eyes fall on the unfinished paintings I had been working on when this all started. I walk over to the paintings that lie piled up in the corner. I pick up the piece that I had been working on the night before getting hospitalized for the first time. I find myself admiring my own work. In a moment of resolve, I decide that I will finish what I started. I set up my easel and get out my brushes, palette, and tubes of colors.

The piece I had been working on was of Waimea Bay, a beautiful wide crescent of sand located on the North Shore. I am fascinated by Waimea Bay, and how this particular body of water changes character so dramatically depending on the season. In the summer, it is glassy still, calm, and inviting. In the winter, swells bring in monstrous waves, heavy and thick. It occurs to me now that Waimea Bay is kind of bipolar, with her moody swings every season, alternating between calm and stormy. I had chosen to portray Waimea's stormy face for my painting and had been working on mixing colors to show the depth and texture of the heavy water in the winter. Water molecules are always made up of the same two hydrogen and single oxygen atoms, but depending on the color of the sky, the wind, and the movement of the water itself, it either appears light or heavy. Waimea in the winter is definitely heavy.

When I paint, my mind feels clear. All the usual static that bombards my thoughts gets quieter, and eventually silences as I pick up my brush, dip it in color, and touch it to the canvas surface. The whole world gets still, the brush becomes an extension of my own body, and I feel myself dancing with the surface I'm painting on. The colors move beneath my strokes like footprints on a path. With watercolors, the water takes over and spreads in ways that I do not expect or plan for. I delight in these moments of surprise. The painting has a will of its own, and l let it have a conversation with me.

The watercolors give me the freedom to express the subtlety of everything I want to express. The exact right color and stroke can express so much more about how I feel on the inside than words could ever capture. I can express the whole world through color. As I dip my brush into the water container to swirl it clean before loading the next color, I find myself drawn back into a world where for a moment, I forget I have bipolar disorder. It is only a moment, but it is the first moment since I have been diagnosed that I feel completely myself again. With that weight momentarily lifted, I realize how much the burden of my diagnosis has been weighing me down every waking and sleeping moment of my being, like a cancer that can't be removed. I hate my bipolar mind. And yet here, in this unexpected moment of discovery, I realize that when I paint, I no longer feel mentally ill. I don't feel Vietnamese or American. I feel like I belong. I feel right. I feel normal. It is a feeling I need to remember and return to.

Chapter 27 - Xuan

1993

I am usually the one who drops Anh off at her weekly appointments with Dr. Tanaka. But today Long has the day off from work so he comes along with us.

As we wait in the waiting room, I ask Long, "Do you think she'll have to take medication the rest of her life?"

"The doctor said it was too early to tell," Long replies.

"I hope not. Have you seen how fat she has gotten on the medication? Do you think she'll still be able to go to college?" I ask anxiously.

"I think so. Dr. Tanaka says that bipolar disorder shouldn't prevent her from doing the things she wants to do."

"Who will want to marry her? Will we have to tell their family that she has this illness?" I can't help myself from worrying about all the unanswered questions in our daughter's future. The worst part is I wonder if this would have happened to Anh if we had stayed in Vietnam. Perhaps it is our punishment for abandoning our country. I feel guilty that I was the one who persuaded us to come to America. Long didn't want to leave. He felt a loyalty to his battered country. He did not find it honorable to leave a bad situation. I was the one who convinced him to go, even after my parents would not agree to come with us. I felt a responsibility to my future children to give them the best opportunity for a happy and successful life. And now look at what happened to Anh. It must be all my fault.

Chapter 28 - Anh

1993

I sit anxiously in the lobby of my guidance counselor's office. I have a meeting scheduled that afternoon to talk about my college applications. Because I was in the hospital twice last semester, I haven't completed my college applications yet like most of my classmates have already done. Now it is already January, and multiple application deadlines have already passed. The purpose of today's meeting is for my advisor Mr. Hoshino to recommend which colleges I still have a chance at being admitted to, and how to explain my absences from the first semester, which led to several incomplete marks on my report card.

Mr. Hoshino is a slim man, tall by Asian standards. He has been a college advisor at Punahou for over 20 years and prides himself on helping the school maintain its impeccable college acceptance and matriculation rates. He is dressed in a crisp navy suit jacket, khaki slacks, and a striped tie, as if he is always ready to host a prospective parent or student or visiting college admissions counselor on a tour of our beautiful campus.

The door to his office opens, and the student who had been meeting with him shuffles out. "Hello, Anh, come in, have a seat while I just finish up some paperwork," Mr. Hoshino says without looking up from the pile of papers on his desk.

I sit down on one of the brown wooden chairs arranged in front of his desk. While I wait, I look around at the diplomas, photographs, and art that he has framed on his walls. I see that he went to college at a school I've never heard of – Carnegie Mellon. What a funny-sounding name. A picture behind his desk is of him and, I assume, his wife and their two teenage children, a boy and a girl. They are at a luau, all wearing matching aloha wear. Before I can figure out what is in the next photograph, Mr. Hoshino clears his throat and begins.

He pulls out a manila envelope with my name written on the tab. "So, Anh, from your file here, it looks like we have not applied to any colleges or universities yet, is that correct?"

"No, I mean yes, that's correct, I haven't applied anywhere yet," I answer nervously.

"Do you still plan on attending college in the fall?" Mr. Hoshino asks me evenly as he looks me directly in the eyes.

I instinctively avert my eyes away from his direct gaze. "Yes, of course. I mean, I've always planned on going to college."

"Good, I'm glad to hear that. I just wanted to make sure we are on the same page. Sometimes kids who have a tough semester decide they need to take some time off, or a break before entering college," he says casually as if what I went through last semester was a bout of chicken pox or a broken leg.

"No, I've taken enough time off. I want to go to college as planned. But is it too late to apply?" I have overheard my classmates talking about which schools they have applied to, which ones they got secondary applications for, what interviews they had scheduled, and even a few who had applied Early Action and had already received acceptance letters from schools.

"Well, some schools' application deadlines have already passed, but there are still a number of good schools with rolling admissions – meaning you can continue to apply to them as long as there is space available in their class. But we better get this show on the road then," Mr. Hoshino says as he starts to compile a list of schools where he thinks I will have a decent chance of admission. "The good thing is your grades were pretty decent before last semester. You do have several incompletes on your record, so I think it is best to address that directly in your essay answers. Schools have gotten much more understanding of mental health issues, not like how it was when I applied to college 30 years ago. Back then, you wouldn't dare mention anything like that."

"You mean I have to explain what happened last semester? That I was hospitalized at Kahi Mohala?" I am terrified at the thought of disclosing all that. I have never spoken to an adult at my school directly about what happened last semester, what my diagnosis is, and that I'm taking medication.

"Look, Anh, you don't have to tell anyone what you don't want to. It's your private information. But I do think it's best to be honest on your application."

But I wouldn't even know what to say, I think to myself. And I don't feel like getting into details with Mr. Hoshino right now.

"OK, so here is a list of eight schools that I think would be a good fit for you and that are still accepting applications. Go home, look them up, and then come back and we can talk about them more." He hands me a piece of paper with the names of colleges written on them. He stands up and extends his hand for a handshake, as if to usher me out of the office. "Good luck, I'll see you next time." He greets my classmate, who is already waiting outside, "Joel, come in, have a seat while I finish up some paperwork."

The door to Mr. Hoshino's office closes, and I stand there blankly, unsure of what to do next. All of a sudden, I feel panicky. I start to feel nauseous and light-headed, like I'm going to pass out if I don't sit down or get some fresh air or a drink of water. My heart starts pounding, and the air feels very hot and stuffy. I start to see white spots drift into my field of vision. I sit down in the chair in front of the office and close my eyes, waiting and praying for the feeling to pass.

As luck has it, it's Tuesday, the day of my regularly scheduled appointment with Dr. Tanaka. I don't want to go, but I don't want to explain to my mom why I don't want to go. I briefly ponder whether it's possible for me to ask my mom to drop me off for the appointment and instead sneak out of the clinic lobby. But my mom insists on sitting in the waiting room lobby for me during my appointment, so I have no escape.

"Hi Anh, come on in," Dr. Tanaka greets me at 4 pm as usual.

I walk back to Dr. Tanaka's office and sit down. I don't feel like talking today.

"How are you today?" Dr. Tanaka starts as she always does.

"I don't feel like talking today," I reply.

"Is everything OK? Did something happen?" Dr. Tanaka inquires. Over the past few months, I have gotten comfortable talking to Dr. Tanaka and telling her how I feel. She can probably tell that there is something upsetting me today.

"I told you I don't feel like talking today," I say again, unable to control the irritation in my voice.

"OK, we'll just sit quietly then. We don't have to talk if you don't feel like it," Dr. Tanaka says.

"Can I just leave then?" I ask.

"Well, this is your time, Anh, and I don't want us to waste it. You're here, and we can just be together and see if you change your mind about talking."

I roll my eyes. Dr. Tanaka isn't a bad person, but sometimes her overly calm demeanor drives me nuts. What kind of a weirdo is OK sitting in silence staring at someone for 45 minutes?

So we sit there, in silence, for what seems like forever, before I can't stand it anymore. "I just had a meeting with my college counselor, and he gave me a list of eight schools he thinks I should apply to," I finally blurt out.

"Oh, and how do you feel about that?" Dr. Tanaka asks quietly.

"Frickin' overwhelmed. Oh, and he also wants me to write in my application essay what happened last semester, to explain the incompletes on my report card. I still don't even understand what happened to me. How the hell am I supposed to explain it to someone else on a college application?"

"That's a lot for you to take in. I can see why you are feeling overwhelmed. Maybe I can help you sort it all out."

"Everyone just expects me to pick up from where I left off, to move on as if nothing happened. But I don't even understand what happened to me. I know I'm different now somehow. I'm not the same old Anh I was before."

"It's a process that takes time, and it's OK to not know everything yet. But it sounds like high school and college decisions are on a completely different timeline than your own internal processes."

"What do you mean by internal processes?" I ask, genuinely confused. I sometimes have no idea what Dr. Tanaka is talking about and have learned that it's better to ask her to explain herself rather than pretend to understand. Otherwise, she has a tendency to go on and on about certain topics.

"Internal processes means what's going on inside of you, your inner world." More concepts I don't understand.

"Inner world?" I ask again with a confused look on my face. Is Dr. Tanaka going crazy on me?

"Yes, you have a rich world inside of you. Your thoughts, feelings, dreams, hopes, worries, fantasies. These are all experiences that you have inside of you. You can't always tell what someone's inner world is like just by looking at their actions and appearances in the outside world." Dr. Tanaka explains.

This whole idea of an inner world is a completely foreign concept to me. I have never heard anyone in my life mention this before. Do my parents have inner worlds?

"Does everyone have an inner world?" I ask curiously.

"Yes, everyone has access to their inner world, but some people pay more attention to it than others. And sometimes people forget, or never realize, that they have this inner world right inside of them."

"What's the point of your inner world? Is it just for fun, like your imagination?"

"Well, that's a really interesting question, and different people have different answers to that. But I personally believe that the more you know and pay attention to your inner world, the more you will be able to direct your external life in a way that honors your true self."

"You mean, so that your inner world and your external world are in sync?" I ask.

"Exactly!" Dr. Tanaka exclaims, as if I had just figured out the answer to some complicated math problem.

"So what does this have to do with my college applications?" I ask again, feeling like I needed to get the doctor back on track.

"Well, you've just had a major event happen in your life last semester, and it's completely normal for you to feel like you're still trying to figure it out. Your inner world is probably very confused by what happened. And the thought of graduating high school and applying to college, which are huge events in and of themselves, probably feels like too much for you to handle."

"But I have to go to college. I have no choice."

"I'm not saying don't go to college. I'm just saying it's understandable that you feel overwhelmed. And acknowledging your inner experience of feeling overwhelmed will help you develop more compassion for yourself."

I am getting lost again. "Why do I need compassion for myself? I just want to be normal." In that moment, for some reason I feel my chest get warm and tears well up in my eyes. I've never cried in front of anyone before. I feel embarrassed and scared, but I can't stop myself.

"I can see you're scared about this," Dr. Tanaka says softly. "And I want you to know that you're not alone. You don't have to do this all by yourself. Your family and I will be here to help you through this."

I close my eyes and continue to feel the hot tears streaming down my cheeks.

Dr. Tanaka sits there silently, allowing me to cry without rushing to stop me or soothe me. After what seems like a very long time, I grab a tissue from the Kleenex box she keeps on the small table next to my chair and dry my eyes. The tears stop, like they have run their course.

"How do you feel now?" Dr. Tanaka asks gently.

"I surprisingly feel a little better. I've never allowed myself to cry like that before," I admit.

"What kinds of feelings were you having while you were crying?"

"I don't know, I just felt scared, and sad."

"Have there been any other times in your life when you felt that way?"

All of a sudden, for no apparent reason, I have a vivid memory of myself sitting in the backseat of my parent's car driving to preschool. "Well, when I was young, I always got motion-sick on the car ride to preschool every morning. My parents tried to distract me by pointing out buildings in the distance, but it only worked for a few minutes. I always ended up throwing up before we got to school. The car smelled so bad from my vomiting, which only made me more nauseous. My dad always got so mad when I threw up and made a mess in the car. I had to sit with a bag over my mouth every morning on the way to school. There was a traffic light right before the turn into my school's parking lot, and I remember praying to *Phật Bà Quán Thế Âm* every morning that the traffic light would stay red forever so that I wouldn't have to go to school."

"So you were feeling very nervous and scared about school even from a young age," Dr. Tanaka says.

"I guess I've never thought about it that way. I mean I like school, but sometimes it feels like a lot of pressure," I say.

"And how do you handle that pressure?"

"What do you mean?" I ask, confused.

"What do you do when you feel scared or nervous?"

"I don't know. I just deal with it."

"Do you talk to anyone about it?"

"No."

"Have you found some ways to relax your mind and body when you feel that way?"

"No."

"So you've just been trying to deal with it all by yourself?"

"I guess."

"Well, let's work together to find some ways to help you deal with your anxiety so you won't have to feel all alone with it."

"Alright," I answer, still not sure what exactly she means.

I look forward to my weekly appointments with Dr. Tanaka. I'm often surprised at where our sessions end up. At first, I was very anxious, almost unbearably uncomfortable with someone paying so much attention to me. But now I appreciate it. I feel like no one pays as much attention to my thoughts and feelings as much as Dr. Tanaka does. I find myself getting annoyed at my parents when they don't understand my feelings, even when I try to explain it to them. My mom has stopped asking me what Dr. Tanaka and I talk about in our sessions. I'm back in school and have returned to my usual routine which apparently is enough for my parents. They have moved on, as if whatever happened in my life three months ago is something in the past that no longer needs mentioning. Is this how they deal with everything in their life? The war? Leaving their country and families behind?

I start to pay more attention to my feelings and realize that I do have activities that relax me – playing in the ocean and painting. I don't fight myself or hate myself when I am in the ocean or painting. I'm not my enemy when I'm behind the easel or on a boogie board. I work with myself rather than against myself. I actually enjoy myself. Maybe that's why I enjoy painting the ocean so much – it's combining my two favorite activities. Since my hospitalizations, I find myself experimenting with acrylic paints more than watercolor. I need a heavier pigment to express what I am feeling inside, I need something darker and heavier to ground me than the delicate light of watercolors.

My first art teacher, Mrs. Rose, liked watercolors, so that was what she introduced me to, and I fell in love with them. But now, as I experiment with the thicker and heavier weight of acrylics, I feel more emboldened. I can be less tentative and more forceful with my strokes. I like how I can make mistakes and then just cover them up, like a secret that only the painting and I know about. Only I know what lies underneath and what it took to get to the final product.

I finish my watercolor ocean series and start on an acrylic sky series capturing the different colors and moods of the sky at different times of day – the light softness of the morning, the glaring contrasts of midday, the warm and sometimes fiery finales of sunset, and the luminous coolness of twilight. I marvel at the infinite spectrum of light and clouds and shadow and color throughout the day. I can't help but think that God, or whoever is the creator of this world, is an artist who enjoys painting the canvasses of the sky each day.

I sit down to start writing my college application essays. But I can't find the right way to start. How do I explain in words what I have gone through in the past year without sounding like a crazy person? *The first time I was hospitalized, I lost it in my English class. The second time was because I was delusional about a tsunami.* That sure doesn't sound like someone I would admit to my school. I stare at the blank screen on my computer and am at a loss for words. I wish I could submit a portfolio of my art pieces rather than a written essay. I could paint them a picture to show how the last year of my life felt. I briefly entertain the idea of applying to an art school for college, but I dismiss the idea when I imagine in my head how the conversation would go with my parents...

"Mom, Dad, I've decided I'm going to go to art school for college."

"What do you mean?" my mom would ask anxiously. "You mean take art classes in college?"

"No, go to a school that specializes in art, to study art."

"To do what?"

"I don't know, to become an artist?"

At that point, my father would start raising his voice to put an end to the ridiculous conversation, "Stupid idea! Art is for fun. Not for studying. How do you make money being an artist? Xuan, I told you we allowed her to spend too much money on her art supplies. Now look at how foolish she is being. Do you think you can just keep buying art supplies and making art to feed your family?"

I know I can't come up with a counterargument to satisfy my parents, or even myself, regarding the logic of going to art school. All I know is that when I paint, I feel the most like myself. I often hear my parents arguing about me behind their thin, closed bedroom door. They seem under enough stress without me bringing up this crazy idea about art school or wanting to become an artist. I'll just have to find a way to do it on the side like I do now.

Chapter 29 - Anh

1993

"I feel this heaviness in my chest. I don't know what it is, but it's always been here," I share with Dr. Tanaka.

"I feel it too when you talk about it," Dr. Tanaka says to me. "It feels like a heavy sadness."

"But I've felt it since I was a little girl. What am I so sad about?"

"I think that is something worth figuring out. And sometimes sadness gets passed on from generation to generation. It may not even be all your own grief."

"You mean some of this may not be mine?

"That's right."

"Well then, whose is it? My parents? My grandparents?"

"Possibly."

"But how does it get passed onto me? I've never even met some of my grandparents."

"Life works in mysterious ways."

"Is it my karma? My mom always says that good or bad things happen to us because of our karma, what we did in our past lives." I say, wondering whether Dr. Tanaka believes in past lives or not.

"Whether it's karma or genetics or environment, children and their parents and grandparents share a deep connection that gets transmitted from womb to womb," she says.

I'm surprised that Dr. Tanaka is talking to me about karma and my ancestors. It's not what I would expect a doctor to do, but as I've gotten to know her better, I've learned that Dr. Tanaka is different from other doctors I've met. Dr. Tanaka encourages me to share my dreams with her. All of a sudden, I remember a dream I had the previous night. "Last night, I had this weird dream about having all these dead dry leaves stuck in my hair. There were so many of them that it would take forever to untangle them out. I was also wearing a red jacket, and when I reached into the pockets, there were more of these dead leaves in my pockets, but only a few handfuls of them that could easily be shaken out, not like the ones in my hair."

"Hmmm, what do you make of the dead leaves?" Dr. Tanaka asks.

"I don't know."

"Any thoughts or ideas about the dream?"

"I just really wanted to get the dead leaves off of me, but they were so tangled up in my hair that I didn't know if I could ever get them all out."

"How did you feel in the dream?"

"Just numb. I didn't feel scared or frantic. Just confused. About how all these leaves got into my hair and how to get them out."

When I can't offer any more thoughts or associations about the dream, Dr. Tanaka gives me her interpretation of the dream, "Well, the fact that the leaves were dead makes me think that they could be related to that sadness and heaviness you're feeling in your chest. The sadness and dead leaves are all tangled up in your hair, but they're not really a part of you. You've picked them up somewhere, maybe from your ancestors and their sadness. It might be hard, but you can wash them out of your hair."

I do not know how to respond. All I can feel is the same deep heaviness in my chest and throat. It is like a stagnant energy that has nowhere to go except linger.

"How can I get it off of me?" I ask desperately. "I would need to take a really long shower."

"Well, it does take time to untangle. Your body is too smart to let you get rid of these things without sorting through them first. You might be surprised at what hidden jewels we can find inside all of these dead leaves of grief. We carry the things we carry for a reason, until we're ready to understand them, learn from them, and then let them go when we've gotten what we needed from them," Dr. Tanaka explains.

"You mean, like this is something my ancestors have passed down to me, and I don't want to throw it out before I go through it?"

"That's a really good way to look at it," Dr. Tanaka says.

I know that Bà nội and my parents put a lot of importance on remembering our ancestors. They do everything they can to avoid dishonoring them. I remember what Bà nội said about learning from our past and our roots. I want to learn the lessons my ancestors are trying to teach me, but I don't want to have dead leaves tangled up in my hair forever. Is there a way I can wash out my hair and let the water clean out the lessons for me, or do I have to shave my head of hair off and start fresh all over again?

CHAPTER 30 - XUAN

1993

It is *Tết*, Lunar New Year, the Year of the Rooster. *Tết* is the biggest holiday in Vietnam. In our Vietnamese family, paying respect to one's ancestors on the anniversaries of their deaths are the most important days to observe. If one does not fulfill one's obligations towards one's ancestors, bad luck will prevail.

Tết, on the other hand, is a time for pure celebration. In Vietnam, my family spent the days and weeks leading up to *Tết* cleaning our house, buying and cooking food, shopping for new clothes and outfits to wear, flowers to decorate the house, and making plans to visit with friends and family. *Tết* is a time to celebrate surviving another year. Sharing food, music, and fireworks is a way to acknowledge all the hard work and sacrifice of the previous year, with hopes for continued health, prosperity, and good fortune in the coming year.

In Hawaii, I notice that most people refer to Lunar New Year as "Chinese New Year" and "*Kung Hee Fat Choy,*" the Chinese way to say, "Happy New Year" is more commonly known than the Vietnamese "*Chúc Mừng Năm Mới.*" Instead of shops and businesses closing down for weeks as they do in Vietnam, Lunar New Year is not even an observed holiday in the United States. It is marked by a label on the American calendars in the same way Flag Day or Groundhog Day is indicated – noted but not important enough for people to get any time off from work. So if Lunar New Year falls on a weekday, we usually celebrate it on the weekend prior to or after the actual day. Our *chùa*, or temple, hosts a gathering which is a more elaborate and festive version of the usual weekend services. The main prayer hall is scrubbed clean until it sparkles, and the altar is filled with colorful and abundant displays of fruit and flowers. The monks perform a special prayer service followed by lion dancing and a vegetarian lunch. Children receive red *lì xì* money envelopes stuffed with a few coins or dollar bills.

Anh and Jack complain about having to go to *chùa*.

"It's so boring," Jack whines to me. "All we do is sit for hours on the ground chanting words that I don't even know the meaning of. I'd rather be at home watching TV."

"And that is exactly why you must go to *chùa*. Watching American TV all day will spoil your mind and ruin your eyesight," I say to them. "All year you go to school with your American friends. This is the only time you get a taste for what being Vietnamese is all about." I feel that this year is an especially important one for our family to show our gratitude for Anh's recovery from her illness, and to pray for continued health and well-being for our family in the coming year, so I drag Jack and Anh to the temple and ignore their complaining.

Chapter 31- Anh

1993

It is the night of my high school graduation. The bright lights shining down from the ceiling of the Neil Blaisdell Arena are hot and almost blinding, so I can't see the darkened audience, but only my fellow classmates on stage with me, the last time we would all gather and be illuminated as one. The girls in my class are wearing beautiful white holoku dresses and haku leis on their heads, while the boys are sharply dressed in navy blue blazers and khaki pants. We look very nice. The dean is giving a farewell speech to our class. It is his tradition to dub each graduating class with an adjective that describes them as a whole. I am curious about what word he will choose for our class. It is one of the few things about the night that is left as a surprise for our class after we had spent the last few weeks in the school gym rehearsing the songs and dances we are going to perform tonight.

I don't know how I feel about graduating from Punahou tonight. A part of me is happy and relieved that I made it. There were times when I wasn't sure if I would actually graduate on time, much less be headed off to college in the fall. But Mr. Hoshino helped me through the college application process, and I was accepted into UC Davis in the fall. It will be a new beginning there. No one will know what I went through last year. Another part of me feels like a fake, like I'm just going through the motions and playing the part, that I am not really here, that this is not really happening to me, that I'm watching someone else's life. I feel both sad and nostalgic about this moment in my life, aware that a chapter of my life is ending tonight while I'm not sure if I'm ready for the next chapter yet. I'm terrified of growing up and having to face the world all by myself.

I feel overwhelmed by all of these conflicting feelings. I try to remember what Dr. Tanaka tells me about allowing myself to feel my emotions without needing to change or control them. Dr. Tanaka is somewhere in the audience, along with my family. I invited her to the ceremony, and she accepted.

The dean continues on with his address, "I have witnessed the kindness and thoughtfulness your class has demonstrated to each other in times of hardship. Your class cares about one another and the common bond you share. Your class is 'communal.'" There is an audible murmuring of reaction amongst my classmates. Communal? What does that mean? Like a communal bathroom? Does it share the same word root as communism? I'm not exactly sure what to make of the word. It definitely isn't a flashy word. It has all the glitter of a brown burlap sack. What a letdown. I can tell that my classmates are also not impressed. There is a *communal* sense of disappointment among us. The dean finishes up his remarks and makes his way back to his seat in the front row while the music conductor makes his way back to center stage. He turns to face us, the graduates, and holds up his conductor's wand in mid-air before dropping his arm to cue the orchestra to start playing the last song of the evening - Aloha 'Oe. As my classmates and I start to sing the Hawaiian words to this farewell song, I can't stop the chicken-skin from forming on my arms and spreading tingling down the rest of my body all the way to my feet. Tears well up in my eyes, and I try my best to hold them back so they won't smear my eyeliner and mascara. A warm wave of emotion sweeps over my entire body. It is indescribable. I wonder if this is how a baby feels right before it comes out of its mother's womb. There is no going back.

CHAPTER 32 - ANH

1993

There are big balloons and banners with the blue and bronze colors of UC Davis welcoming new students to campus. I hold a piece of paper that tells me I have been assigned to the dorm Bixby Hall and that my roommate is someone named Jessica from Petaluma, California. The campus is huge, and I wonder how I will ever find my way around it. Davis is supposed to be a bike-friendly town, and most people got around on and off campus by bicycle. That is great, except that I don't know how to ride a bike. That was something that my parents didn't think was a necessary skill in America, where everyone has cars. My parents had flown with me from Hawaii to the mainland to settle me into my freshman dorm. We eventually find our way to the north side of campus, where my residence hall is located. There is a check-in folding table set up in front of the dorm.

"Hi! Welcome to Bixby Hall!" an overly enthusiastic student shouts at us. "What's your name? I'm Scott, and I'll be one of your resident assistants."

"I'm Anh Nguyen," I say.

"How do you spell your last name?" Scott asks.

Here we go again, I think. "N-G-U-Y-E-N," I rattle off. I have gotten so used to spelling my last name for people that it has become almost a familiar tune to my ears, like A-B-C.

"There you are," Scott says as he finds my name in the row of folders lined up in the box. "From Honolulu, Hawaii, eh? That's cool. I think there's someone else here in Bixby from Hawaii too," he mentions.

"Really?" I respond. I didn't expect to feel excited about meeting someone else from Hawaii, but I suddenly feel a pang of homesickness. My parents will be going home tomorrow and I will be left here in this new place all by myself. My parents and I have never been particularly sentimental or affectionate with one another, but all of a sudden I want to reach out and grab my mother's hand and tell her not to leave me. But my mother's hands are already holding multiple plastic bags filled with various pens, notepads, stickers, and water bottles that she had picked up around campus that morning. "Let's go see your room," she says to me.

My room is #210 on the second floor. I walk up the tiled steps leading to the second floor with my parents trailing behind. The dorm is clean but exudes that sterile institutional feel that distinguishes dorms, hotels, and hospitals from home. When we get to the second floor, I walk down the long hallway looking for my room number. Halfway down the hallway, I find my room on the left-hand side of the corridor. My roommate has already arrived and set down her bags on a bed, claiming the left side of the room. The room is small, with just enough room for two twin-sized beds, two desks, and two drawers arranged symmetrically down the middle of the room, each side an exact mirror copy of the other. I will be sharing this small space with a stranger for the next year. For a moment, the room triggers a memory of the psychiatric hospital at Kahi Mohala, except it is even smaller than that.

My father has been quiet. He has his hands in his pockets and looks briefly around the small room. He opens his mouth as if he is about to say something, but then decides against it and closes his mouth shut again. My mom is not shy about speaking her thoughts. "Not much room here. You'll have to keep it clean. No room for the mess you keep at home," she says to me. And then, in a softer tone, "Let's go find a place where we can buy you bedsheets and a blanket."

Just then, a pale-faced girl with stringy brown hair and wire-rimmed glasses walks into the room with her parents and a younger brother trailing behind. "Hi, you must be Anh. I'm Jessica. I hope you're OK that I chose this side of the room," she says in a soft voice.

I immediately feel relieved. I had been worrying about who my roommate would be, and this girl looks harmless enough. "Hi. That's fine. Not much difference between the two sides anyway," I say, and we both laugh.

Jessica's parents politely introduce themselves to mine. Her father is a tall, thin man with short-cropped hair and wire-rimmed spectacles that make him look like a professor. "Long way from home, eh?" Jessica's father says, addressing his comment to no one in particular.

My mom nods her head in agreement. "Yes, mainland colleges are good, better than Hawaii."

Jessica's mother is also a thin woman with short, bobbed hair and a kind face. "How long will you be in town for?" she asks my parents.

"We fly back to Hawaii tomorrow," my father replies.

"So soon?" Jessica's mom looks concerned. "Well, we only live an hour away, so don't worry, we'll help Anh if she needs anything," she offers reassuringly.

"Thank you so much," my mom reaches out to grab Jessica's mom's hands to shake them in gratitude.

As I settle into my freshman dorm, I marvel at how often some of my dormmates' parents visit or contact them. Even those families that do not live locally send care packages or call frequently on the phone. Even when I lived at home, I barely had conversations with my parents about anything more than cursory comments about it being time for dinner. It does not seem odd to me that my parents view their main duty in supporting me through college is by paying my tuition bills every quarter. What is more foreign is witnessing how involved other parents or families are with their college-aged children.

One night Jessica and I are hanging out together in our dorm room. Jessica has started putting up posters of her favorite bands on the wall – U2 and The Beatles – and I feel embarrassed that I haven't brought anything to put up on my walls. I hadn't even thought of decorating the walls. Back home, the walls in my room were bare. My parents did not invest much value in interior decorating. My parents worried about other things they deemed more important, like money and business, to consider what might look nice on the walls. I now feel exposed, that everyone can see me for how worthless I am. I don't have anything of value to add to this dorm or this school. They must have made a mistake in admitting me, and soon they will realize it.

"Do you know what classes you're going to take yet?" Jessica asks as she flips casually through the course catalog. "Can you believe they offer a class on sex?" she asks incredulously. The course catalog is an overwhelming public phone-book-sized publication that literally lists thousands of course offerings in every imaginable department. UC Davis gives every freshman a list of required classes and units that they are expected to take at some point in their four years here. It is up to us to decide what courses to take first and how many to take. At one of the academic orientation tables, I grabbed a handout that lists the prerequisite classes needed to apply for medical school. I'm not sure if I want to become a physician, but my parents have been talking about it so long that I might as well see what it takes to be pre-med. The list of required classes starts as early as the first quarter of college and includes classes like organic chemistry and math. I scan a sample four-year plan of a premedical student and see that there are lecture and laboratory classes in biology and chemistry almost every quarter, leaving very little room to explore other interests. I'm interested in art and art history classes, but pre-med requirements don't leave much room for exploring much else. I envy Jessica's casual approach to choosing classes, as if they are desserts in a pastry shop, to be tried and discarded if found unpleasant. To me, choosing classes feels like choosing the direction of my entire life, and that decision will lead to success or failure, my parents' approval and pride, or disapproval and rejection.

"I'm not sure yet. What about you?" I learn that it is easy to deflect attention back to someone else with a question of your own. People are always eager to talk about themselves, and then you don't have to talk about yourself.

"Well, I want to be a writer," Jessica shares somewhat sheepishly. "So I want to take some creative writing classes. But I don't know, I'm not sure yet either."

"That's cool that you want to be a writer. What do your parents say about that?" I ask, genuinely curious what Jessica's parents think about such a career aspiration.

"They're supportive of it. They want me to do whatever makes me happy." The way Jessica talks about her relationship with her parents seems like a foreign universe to me. Emboldened by Jessica's approach to her education, I flip to the Art Department section and browse through their offerings. Again, a dizzying array of options, from Ceramics to Sculpting to Glass Blowing to Film Making. The painting courses are listed by medium, genre, and time period, and rated from beginner to professional. A particular course title catches my eye – "Healing With The Arts." I read the description of the course taught by a physician who uses various art media as "a way to heal the mind, body, and spirit." I recall an art therapy exercise I participated in while I was at Kahi Mohala during my second hospitalization. An art therapist had come to the unit and led us through an exercise of creating a "landscape of our feelings." The teacher encouraged everyone to explore different colors and images to create a visual depiction of how we felt. I enjoyed the exercise and have always known how therapeutic painting is for me. I circle the course number with my pencil and note that it meets on Wednesday and Friday evenings from 6-8 pm in Crawley Hall. The course is Pass/Fail and will give me three units toward my elective course requirements. It seems like a safe place to start. I can also tell my parents that a doctor teaches the course.

UC Davis is located inland, far from the sea. The land is flat and primarily agricultural. I miss the ocean. The closest beach to me now is at least a 90-minute drive away, and I don't have a car. I barely know how to ride my bike around campus without crashing into poles and curbs.

"I really miss the beach," I sigh to Jessica one Saturday morning. It's a rare day when we're both in our dorm room, sitting in our beds, trying to figure out what to do.

"Let's go then," Jessica replies with a sparkle in her eyes. "I have a car, it's not that far to San Francisco. I know a beach we can go to." She hops off of her bed and starts planning excitedly for our day. "We can drive across the Golden Gate Bridge, go to Baker Beach, and then grab food somewhere in the city. It's going to be so much fun!"

That does sound exciting. I recall picturesque views of San Francisco in the opening scenes of the TV show *Full House* and imagine that "The City" is an exciting playground of buildings, shops, people, and sights. There is nothing like it in Hawaii. But then a wave of anxiety hits me. It's so far away, I don't have time to go, I need to stay back and study, even though classes have barely started. I am not good with spontaneity and impulsive decisions.

"You mean go today? I don't think so, I have to study," I reply, aware of how lame I sound.

"It's Saturday, you can study tomorrow. This is what being in college is all about. You don't have to ask permission or tell your parents your plans, we can just decide to get in the car and go!" Jessica exhorts. I swear I feel like I'm her pet project. She thinks I'm a boring nerd who needs to have more fun. If I don't go, I'll never hear the end of it all weekend.

"Alright, alright, I'll go, but let's not get back too late," I say, feeling a mixture of both adventure and anxiety. Going to San Francisco for the day does sound exciting, and I'll get to see the ocean again!

Jessica pops in a music CD in her Honda Civic, and we start our drive down "to the Bay Area," as I've often heard my dormmates say. As we near the Golden Gate Bridge, traffic slows down to nearly a crawl, but I don't mind because I am in awe of this spectacular structure. The bold, blood-red bridge stretches up and out before me. We slowly inch our way across the Bay. I can't take my eyes off of the bridge, marveling at the thick coiled metal ropes and large bolts and screws that are holding this enormous construction together. It looks exactly like it does in the movies. And there are tons of people walking and biking across the bridge on both sides.

"Do you want to walk across the bridge?" Jessica asks me. "It'll be hard to find parking in this mess," she says. I do want to walk across the bridge, but I don't want to inconvenience my friend, who has already driven me down all this way.

"That's OK, we're going slow enough, it's almost like I'm walking," I reply. "Maybe next time when it's not so crowded."

Jessica laughs, "It's always crowded, but good call. Let's go straight to Baker Beach then."

It is a cloudy day, and I am disappointed by the color of the ocean. The ocean has no color, just the muddy gray you get when you mix too many colors together. I miss the clear turquoise and deep green-blue colors of the ocean in Hawaii.

I am wearing shorts and a t-shirt and slippers, and the air is cold. I didn't think to bring a jacket to the beach and now I am getting goosebumps. I miss feeling the sun warm my skin. I look around and am surprised at how many people go to the beach fully clothed in jeans, shirts, and even covered shoes! It doesn't feel right to go to the beach wearing so much clothing. But whatever, I'm finally at the ocean again. I kick off my slippers and head toward the water. I run to the water's edge and let the water come up and swirl around my ankles. I recoil at the freezing temperature of the water – no wonder there's hardly anyone in it!

"The water is freezing!" I yell to Jessica.

"What did you expect?" she laughs back. "This isn't Hawaii!"

I'm not sure what I was expecting. All I know is that I needed to see the ocean again, even if it looks different. I close my eyes and, for a moment, just listen to the sound of the waves rhythmically crashing on the shore. The air feels cold on my cheeks, and the salty water smells different, but the ocean sounds the same everywhere.

After we walk up and down the beach and take some pictures, Jessica suggests we go to Chinatown and get some dim sum. The Chinatown in San Francisco is so much bigger than the Chinatown in Hawaii, which is only a few blocks long. Everything on the mainland is bigger and different, and I always feel like I'm the one that doesn't fit in, wherever

I am. I remember not fitting in with my lunchbox in kindergarten, or moving to Punahou in fifth grade, or pretending to be normal at school after my hospitalizations. And now I feel like I don't quite fit in here either. Why does everyone else look so comfortable while I always feel like I'm the foreigner? Will I ever fit in anywhere?

When we get back to Davis that night, I am tired from our long day in the City, but Jessica is already making plans to go out.

"Hey Anh, there's a party at the Sig Ep frat house tonight. My boyfriend's rushing there. You want to come with us?" Jessica asks. My first impression of Jessica was that she was a bookish girl. I imagined her spending nights curled up in bed with a book. However, Jessica turns out to be more of a party girl than I expected. Jessica goes out every Friday and Saturday night and often comes back to our dorm room in the middle of the night after I have long gone to bed.

"No, that's OK," I reply.

"Oh, come on, Anh! It's Saturday night. You always stay in. Let's go out and have some fun," Jessica encourages.

"Maybe next time," I give another excuse.

"It's still early in the quarter. Soon we'll actually have to start studying," Jessica laughs as she applies eyeliner on in front of the mirror hanging on her wardrobe door.

"I promise next time," I say. I am not one for spontaneity. I have to physically and mentally prepare myself for the idea of getting dressed up and going to a party where I won't know anyone.

"OK, next time then," Jessica replies breezily as she checks her reflection in the mirror one last time before leaving.

I'm alone in my dorm room. It's Saturday night and I hear the excited chattering of other dormmates down the hallway making plans for their evening. I have a flashback to sitting in the girls' bathroom at Punahou, listening to the popular girls laugh about their weekend plans. Am I always going to be on the outside of every social circle? College is supposed to be a new beginning, a fresh start, and here I am, repeating the same social pattern again from high school. *I'm such a loser. I'll never make friends.*

Chapter 33 - Xuan

1993

The house is quieter now that Anh has gone off to college. Jack is usually in his room or out with his friends and we only see him at mealtimes. On the night of Anh's graduation from Punahou, a mother of one of Anh's classmates tells me how much she is going to miss her daughter when she leaves for college. "How do you think you'll manage?" this lady asked me. I did not know what she meant or how to answer her question. Americans seem to make such a big deal about their feelings, and talking about their feelings. Vietnamese people do what we have to do, and life goes on. Of course I'll manage. Anh is going off to college, not war. I look at the photo I keep on the nightstand of Long and myself on our wedding day. I am wearing a traditional red *áo dài* dress and am seated on the edge of a bed, slightly turned away from the camera. Long is wearing a tailored black suit and striped tie. He holds a cigarette still burning between his fingers. That day seems like a lifetime ago. Long had walked through town in a traditional procession to my family's home, bearing gifts and offerings to my family.

On that day, the future felt so bright. I was going to be married to a handsome man from a respectable family. Long was kind and thoughtful, and we would have a happy life together. I felt beautiful in my wedding dress and happy that night, celebrating with my friends and family. I promised that I would be a good wife and a good daughter and that I would do whatever it took to make my family proud.

Thinking back to that day, I feel that I disappointed my parents. I decided to leave them and Vietnam to give my children a better future, and now I am not sure if Anh will be OK, if I raised her well enough, if I had done something wrong as a mother or a daughter that caused this mess.

Our neighbors Frank and Mary, who recently retired from Michigan, have invited me and Long over to their house for dinner. I am always curious how American families decorate their homes and how different it is from our own. I marvel at how many things they have whose sole purpose appears to be merely for decoration. That must be the mark of true luxury, being able to buy something that doesn't serve any function besides looking good.

I am curious about a picture lying on the living room table that has been cut up into many pieces. I wonder what happened to it. The picture is of a large brown bear and its cub walking through a grassy field, but there are big holes in the picture where the pieces have not been fit together yet. I ask my neighbor Frank, "What is this?" Frank laughs at the puzzled expression on my face and explains, "This is a jigsaw puzzle. You try and fit the pieces together to make this picture," he says as he holds up a box with the completed picture on it for me to see. "Try it," Frank nudges both me and Long towards the table. Long, who has been standing quietly next to me, politely shakes his head and excuses himself to the restroom.

I sit down in front of the large table and start fingering the edges of the glossy quarter-sized pieces in my hands. I am both curious and confused by the task. Why would anyone cut something up just to put it back together again? Americans must be very rich people if they have time to play games like this. I can't even imagine where most families in Vietnam would even find the space to work on a puzzle in their homes. The one folding card table we used to eat on was quickly folded up after each meal to make room for the sleeping mats to be rolled out. Plus, how do you keep track of all those pieces without losing them? I try fitting two green pieces together. Their shapes look like they would fit, but they don't. All the pieces look very similar. How can I find the exact puzzle piece that fits its adjacent neighbor? I see that whoever has been working on the puzzle started by fitting together the straight-edged pieces that frame the picture. The rest of the pieces are somewhat sorted by color, but since most of the puzzle consists of only two colors – green and brown – that does not help very much. The cub bear is much smaller, and its hair is a lighter brown than its mother so those pieces are the easiest to find. As I sort through the pieces I notice my eyes becoming more accustomed to the subtle shades of green and brown. There are so many different shades of green and brown, not just two colors.

I try fitting together several other pieces and finally find two that fit together exactly. It is satisfying to find two pieces that were once whole finding their place together again. I want to reunite more pieces that have been separated from their neighbors, pieces that have been lost in this sea of color, waiting to be reunited with the one place they belong. If only life were this simple, knowing that there is a way where all the pieces do come together to make a finished picture, where when you reach the end of it, you can look back on your life and say, *This is how it all came together, this is how it all made sense.* Most of the time, my life feels like the thousand puzzle pieces all scattered apart, each one never finding where it belongs. Even if little sections come together, it is a far way from feeling whole. There are too many places where the picture got broken and the fabric got torn to feel like it could ever come back together again in one piece.

"Having fun, are we?" Frank says to me in friendly banter as he approaches the coffee table.

I am startled and, all of a sudden, deeply embarrassed, as if I have been caught in a private pleasurable act. I quickly stand up, but my blood still rushes its way upstream to flush my face with embarrassment. "I'm sorry," I instinctively reply, but not quite sure what I am apologizing for.

"There's nothing to be sorry about. I can use all the help I can get with that puzzle. Those damn green pieces all look the same to me after a while."

I still feel frozen and exposed. "I'll go see if Martha needs help with anything," I manage to finally say and excuse myself to the kitchen.

After dinner, we thank our neighbors for their hospitality and walk back home to our house next door. "They are very nice people," I say to Long, who is already opening our refrigerator to find a familiar taste to snack on. After living in Hawaii for almost 20 years, Long has gotten used to eating local food, but sometimes his hunger for Vietnamese food is insatiable. I feel guilty that I am not a very good cook and there is no pot of *thịt kho* braised meat or *cá kho* caramelized fish sitting on the stove for him to pick on. He closes the refrigerator door without finding anything and eventually settles on a clustered branch of lychee fruit sitting on the kitchen countertop. He grabs one of the small prickly red fruits off of its stem. I watch him holding the strange-looking fruit in the palm of his hand, the color of its stiff rind a dark pink that reminds me of raw flesh rather than an external covering. With the sharp tip of his nail, Long plunges his thumb into the skin of lychee fruit to start an edge to peel. In contrast to the deep pink hue of the outer shell, the inner flesh of the lychee fruit is a translucent bulb of smooth white membrane with faint striations like human wrinkles. When the skin is entirely removed, the naked fruit glistens like an oversized pearl. Long brings the exposed fruit up to his lips and bites into its sweet flesh. I imagine its perfume aroma drifting into his nostrils as its juicy sweetness engulfs his taste buds, cleaning out the lingering taste of meatloaf and mashed potatoes from his mouth.

Chapter 34 - Anh

1993

It's Friday night, and I am debating whether to go to the Healing with the Arts class or not. It would be so much easier to just climb into bed and call it a night. But this is the first class that genuinely interests me, so I decide to get up and leave my dorm room before I change my mind. I unlock my bike and ride it to the Art Department. There is a courtyard in front with a large contemporary sculpture of four rusted metal geometric shapes lined up in a row. A plaque in front of the sculpture notes it is a gift from the Alumni Class of 1954. I walk up the stone steps and past the sculptures to the front door of the building. The catalog lists the class location as Crawley Hall, Room 201. I enter a cool, high-ceilinged building with shiny dark wood floors and a large spiraling staircase in the center of the room. I glance at the black and white directory on the wall and note there are three floors and that Room 201 is located on the second floor. The building is quiet; there is no receptionist seated at the front desk. But then again, it is 6 pm. I wonder whether this is a stupid idea to show up for this class. Who signs up for a Healing with the Arts class on Friday evenings? Probably only a loser like me. Just as I am contemplating whether to walk back out the door, an older-looking gentleman with curly, grey-white hair enters the building carrying a large box filled with various art supplies under one arm and a stack of books under his other arm. He notices the lost expression on my face and asks, "Do you need help? Are you looking for something?"

I freeze for a moment, and then manage to say, "I'm looking for the Healing with the Arts class."

"Oh, good, I'm Donald," he smiles. "I would offer you my hand, but I'm short on them right now," he quips, adding, "I'm teaching the course, so we're headed to the same place." He starts up the stairs with his hands full.

"Can I help you carry something?" I ask, following him up the stairs.

"Thanks for the offer, but I'm afraid if I let go of something right now, everything will come tumbling down. Don't worry, I do this all the time."

I follow Professor Donald up the spiral staircase to the second floor. At the top of the landing, the floor opens up into a large foyer facing the front of the building. The wall is lined with large floor-to-ceiling windows with black frames. Natural light pours in from the large windows in contrast to the dimly lit first floor. Donald walks to the far end of the floor and places down his box and books to get some keys out of his pocket to unlock the classroom door.

"Looks like we're the first ones here," Donald remarks cheerfully.

I worry whether I'll be the only student that shows up. Of all the thousands of students at UC Davis, how can I be the only one to choose this particular course? I tentatively ask, "How many students generally take this class?"

"It really varies. Some years we have 15, some years we only have a handful of students. Don't worry, I've never had only one student show up. But I guess anything is possible!"

It turns out that six others show up that evening for the Healing with the Arts course taught by Professor Donald. He rearranges the tables and chairs in the classroom so that there is a circle of chairs facing each other in the middle of the room. When it becomes clear that no one else is arriving that night, he gets up and removes the empty chairs from the circle and asks those who remain seated to scoot their chairs up into a tighter circle.

"I'm so happy that for one reason or another, we have all found ourselves here together on this lovely fall evening," the professor begins. "I'm going to start by lighting some sage to clear the energy in the room and invite our helping spirits and guides to bless us with their healing and presence this evening." He gets up and walks around the circle of students holding up a smoking bushel of dead leaves and singing some sort of incantation. A girl sitting across from me closes her eyes and starts swaying to the rhythm of the professor's chanting. I have no idea what I have gotten myself into. I look around at the other students in the circle and make eye contact with an Asian guy, and we briefly give each other a look that acknowledges our mutual bewilderment. The guy is kind of cute, in a mainland Asian kind of way.

When Professor Donald finishes his chanting, he enters the middle of the circle and rings a large bowl like the one my grandma uses to pray. He then takes a seat and joins our circle. "Welcome again. I always like to start my class with a ritual to invite the sacred into our ordinary lives, to create a space for us to listen to the messages our bodies and spirits are trying to send to us and through us. As a practicing family physician for the past 30 years, I have been privileged to witness the myriad of ways our souls communicate with us through our illnesses and challenges. The soul expresses itself through our bodies, both physically and emotionally. When we can pay attention to our symptoms and difficulties, we can gain insight into the wisdom of what our lives are trying to teach us. When I work with my patients, we not only focus on taking care of their illness but also on finding the meaning of the illness.

"Let me give you an example. When I was diagnosed with cancer ten years ago, my soul was trying to tell me that I was not taking care of myself as well as I needed to. And by not taking care of myself, I was also not honoring my pledge to my patients to serve them from a place of health and well-being. It was through art that I really began to get in touch with what my soul wanted me to hear. It was such a powerful modality for healing that I felt compelled to share it with others along with my traditional medical practice. What I want to start with today is you becoming more familiar with that inner wisdom that we all carry within us, whether we call it our intuition, our spirit, our soul, or our true selves, it is that part of us that knows what we need and is constantly trying to get us to pay attention to its message. As a physician, I have studied how our minds and bodies work. I believe that this wisdom or intuition is something we all possess. Some of us may be more sensitive to it, or more practiced at listening to it than others, but it is a skill that we can all develop the same way we strengthen a bicep muscle through lifting weights. The way for us to strengthen this skill is to practice paying mindful attention. So we are going to do an exercise to develop our facility with attention. I'm going to lay out on this table various objects, and I want you all to choose one that catches your attention for some reason. Maybe it's beautiful or ugly or colorful, or maybe it evokes a certain feeling in you. Whatever it is, choose an object."

Professor Donald lays out a large collection of objects on the table in the middle of the circle. I scan the pile of objects to choose from. There are numerous animal figures and small treasures – dolphins, owls, dogs, miniature plastic toys of superheroes and Barbie dolls, bird feathers, nests, stones, dried branches, and a dark cauldron with a lid and metal handle. I am drawn to the small cauldron. I choose this object and bring it back to my seat with me. The other students in the class do the same, some taking longer than others to choose their object.

As we settle back into our seats, Professor Donald starts up again, "Now that each of you has chosen an object, I want you to closely observe and describe it. Use all of your senses. How does it look? Feel? Smell? Sound? Taste? Does it bring up any feelings or emotions for you? Does it remind you of anything? What message is it trying to send you?"I lift up the miniature cauldron in my hand. I am pleased by the substantial heft and weight of it, compared to its diminutive size; it isn't something flimsy or easily broken. Its surface is dark grey and smooth except for a raised insignia on one side that looks like two intertwined loops of rope woven together into a Celtic symbol. I open up the lid and peer inside the dark, hollowed interior. The cauldron stands on three legs, each angled with perfect symmetry around its base like a sturdy tripod. The cauldron reminds me of something a witch would use to brew up magic potions. I imagine throwing strange ingredients into the pot, like newt's eye and salamander tail, along with my bipolar illness and a dash of Lithium. I think about throwing in my blood, my parent's tears, my watercolors, my acrylic paints, and mixing all these elements together. What would happen? Would something valuable come out? Could it even be beautiful?

Chapter 35 - Xuan

1993

"I never told you this before, but my uncle killed himself," I confess to Long one night while we are lying side by side in bed. It is a family secret that I have kept to myself for all these years, and I no longer want to carry the weight of it alone.

"How?" Long asks me. This is the first question that pops into his mind.

"He hung himself from the mango tree in our backyard. I was only about five years old, but I saw him. I can still see that image in my mind."

"How come you never told me before?" Long asks.

"I thought you would think that my family was crazy and you wouldn't want to marry me or have children with me." As I say this, I realize just how much shame and sadness I have carried about my uncle for so many years. "My mother was never the same after my uncle died. There was always a deadness in her eyes that didn't refresh after a night's sleep." I think about my mother and feel a heavy knot lodge in my throat. It slowly makes its way down my neck and across the front of my chest to its usual home in my breastbone. Its weight presses down heavily on my chest, making each breath labored. I am surprised at its unexpected arrival, like a rogue wave that comes out of nowhere. In a rare moment of tenderness, Long senses my vulnerability and rolls over onto his side to embrace me. I bury my head in his chest and let tears roll through me like sets of waves.

"Do you think Anh is taking her medication?" I ask Long worriedly.

"I'm sure she is. She's a smart girl," he answers reassuringly.

"Do you think it's our fault that Anh has this illness?" I ask.

"I don't know," Long sighs. "Dr. Tanaka told us that there was nothing we could have done to prevent it."

CHAPTER 36 - ANH

1993

It's the morning of my first organic chemistry class. I walk into the lecture hall, a large room with stadium seating centered facing a lecture podium. An overhead projector displays the title of the class and the name of the professor onto two large screens located behind him. There are literally hundreds of students in the room. I find a seat near the back of the room, feeling overwhelmed by the size of the lecture hall and the number of people in the room. Several TAs walk up and down the aisles handing out the syllabus and schedule for the course, including when the problem sets are due and dates for the quizzes, midterm and final examination, and the location and meeting times for TA sections and office hours. The amount of information I have to take in is dizzying.

I feel my heart pounding faster and the familiar knot in my stomach clench tighter. It all of a sudden becomes uncomfortably hot in the room, and I feel light-headed and dizzy. I open my water bottle and take a few sips of water to see if that will make me feel better. I am afraid I am going to pass out, and don't want that to happen in front of everyone. I have to get out of this room before I pass out. I quickly gather up my papers, notebook, and pen into my backpack and shuffle my way past several seated students to reach the aisle. I make a mental note to always sit at the edge of an aisle in future lectures for easy escape. I still feel light-headed even after I get outside the building and feel the sunlight on my body. I sit down on a bench to see if that will help. *How will I ever get through this course if I can't even make it through one lecture?* I think to myself. *I'm not cut out to be pre-med. I'm a complete failure.* I see students walking and biking by, looking calm and confident. Others are sitting contentedly under the shade of a tree laughing with friends. I imagine that I am the only one who feels lost and confused. I feel paralyzed as to what to do next. Do I try and go back into the lecture hall? Should I go back to my dorm room? I don't know what to do, and the doubt makes my mind spin even faster. *I don't know what to do. I don't know what to do. I can't do this.* I don't know how long I sit there on the bench, my mind racing, trying to figure out what is the right decision, afraid to make the wrong decision, but they all seem wrong.

I can't remember if I took my Lithium this morning or not. I hate taking my medication. It's a constant reminder that something is wrong with me. At home, I didn't like how my parents watched me take my medication like I was some sort of crazy baby. Dr. Tanaka had told them that it was important to ensure that I took it every day and night. I hate taking my medication, but I promised my parents I would continue taking it. The thought had not crossed my mind to stop taking it. I am scared that I might have another episode like the one I had in Hawaii if I stop taking it. But now that I possibly forgot one dose, the idea of skipping another seems more possible. My mind starts to tell me that I should stop taking the medication. *You don't need it. The medication is making it hard for you to concentrate on your studies. You won't be able to pass O-Chem if you take your medication.* That night I don't take my Lithium and notice that I am not as tired. I can stay up later studying, but my brain still has a difficult time taking in all the organic chemistry material that was supposed to be covered in lecture today. Unlike English and art classes, my mind struggles with science. The depictions of letters and lines and dots that are supposed to represent elements and compounds and electrons and their bonds and the ways they interact with one another do not come naturally to me. Trying to make sense of the material makes my head hurt. If I can't even get through the first month of classes, how can I ever make it through the rest of college? I slam my chemistry textbook shut and bang my head down against my desk.

Chapter 37 - Anh

1993

Bixby Hall is a co-ed dorm, so there are rooms with both boys and girls on my floor. Right across the hallway from me are Matt and John. Matt is from Alaska, and John is from Stockton, somewhere in California. California is so big, I seem to keep meeting people from different parts of California, and I have no idea where they all are on a map. This is my first time living on the mainland away from home, and everything is so new. In our dorm, leaving our door open invites other dormmates to come in and hang out in our rooms. I am not used to being around so many other people. It makes me nervous, and I usually keep mine and Jessica's door closed when it's just me in the room. I am sitting at my small wooden desk, poring through the Fall Quarter class catalog one more time. It's still the shopping period for classes, the two weeks at the beginning of the quarter when we can try out a bunch of different classes before committing to our schedule. I am agonizing over what classes to take. I need to take Organic Chemistry to stay on the pre-med track, along with the required English and Humanities. I really want to take that Healing with the Arts class I visited last week, but it doesn't fulfill any requirements besides elective credit. I can't make a decision, afraid that I'll make the wrong one and not be able to take it back and do it over again. Everything feels like so much pressure.

I hear a slight knock on my door, and I almost jump up in reaction. Who's knocking on my door? I get up and answer the door and am surprised to see my dorm mate Matt standing in front of my door.

"Uh, hi, Anh. Have you eaten yet? I was just going to get lunch at the dining hall and was wondering if you wanted to go together?" Matt asks nervously.

I feel my face flush slightly warm and red, and my heart starts to pound a little faster. I don't know what to say. Matt is kinda cute, and I have never had a boy ask me to anything before. I didn't date anyone in high school. My parents wouldn't have allowed it, and I was too shy anyway.

I just stand there processing all of this in my head while Matt shifts back and forth from side to side. He looks nervous too. I wasn't really hungry yet, but decide, why not say yes?

"Sure, Matt, I'll go to the dining hall, let me just grab my ID card," I manage to say as I close the door on him and go back into my room to grab my ID card and keys from my desk. This will be a welcome distraction to figuring out what classes to take. I look at myself in the mirror and flip my fingers through my hair to make myself look slightly cuter than I feel.

"Alright, let's go," I say as I came out of my room. We walk across the courtyard to the dining hall literally across the way from us. I pick up a meal tray and make my way through the endless food options – salads, sandwiches, soups, hot entrees, and endless dessert choices. I miss Bà nội's Vietnamese cooking, but I have to say, the food at the dining hall is pretty good. And with my meal plan, it's like eating at a restaurant buffet of choices every meal. I decide to get a hot turkey sandwich and a slice of cherry pie. I have been eating dessert with every meal. Matt has gotten a burger and fries and a chocolate milkshake. We "pay" for our meals with our meal plan cards and find an empty table next to the windows.

"What's it like to grow up in Hawaii?" Matt asks me as we sit down.

"It's pretty awesome. Life's a beach," I say and laugh nervously. God, did I really just say "Life's a beach?" How stupid sounding is that?

"What's it like to grow up in Alaska?" I ask quickly to divert the attention away from me.

"Uh, pretty cool too, I guess. I work on my dad's fishing boat a lot."

"Really? What do you catch?"

"Mostly salmon. It's hard work. My dad and my grandpa and my family have been fishermen for a long time. I don't think that's what I want to do, though."

"What do you want to do?" I ask.

"I'm not sure yet. That's what we're here to figure out, right?" Matt says casually.

It shocks me how many of my classmates tell me that they don't know what they want to do with their lives yet. My parents have told me since the fifth grade that I am going to be a doctor. In my family, the only question I asked myself was, "Do I really want to be a doctor?" rather than "What do I want to do?" Becoming a doctor was the default expectation, and unless I could come up with enough reasons why I didn't want to be a doctor, there was nothing else to consider. I liked my pediatrician, and I liked Dr. Tanaka. Doctors made good money and were well-respected. Being a doctor didn't seem like the worst thing that could happen to you.

"What about you?" Matt asks me.

"Um, I'm taking pre-med classes to apply to medical school," I answer.

"So you wanna be a doctor, huh?"

"Yes...I guess," I say, for the first time questioning myself.

"Well, it's only the second week of school. More importantly, what are you doing this weekend?" Matt asks me. He seems to be more comfortable now.

"Uh, I was planning on studying. Organic chemistry is really confusing me," I reply. I sound really boring, even to myself.

"Well maybe after you study, we can go have some fun too." He smiles at me, and I feel a strange sensation in my stomach that I haven't felt before.

"Yeah, I'd like that. Just knock on my door," I tell him. "It's good for those of us from non-contiguous continental states to stick together," I say, making some small attempt at humor. We both laugh at my joke, which isn't even that funny.

Chapter 38 - Anh

1993

It is a Saturday night, and I don't realize how cool the air is until I get outside. I still forget how cool evenings are in California, even when the days have been warm. But I don't feel like going back up to my dorm room to grab a jacket, so I continue walking in the brisk air. I walk out onto Russell Blvd, a road that borders the north edge of campus. The bright lights of the football field shine through the leaves of the trees, and I can hear the thumping beat of music. As I continue walking down the street, the music gets louder, and I hear voices laughing outside. The music is coming from a house down the street that has Greek letters hanging over the front doorway, representing some fraternity. I think about turning around, so I don't have to walk by the party, but a part of me is also curious to see what a fraternity party is all about. I stand still in the middle of the sidewalk. It has become more difficult for me to make decisions, even simple ones.

My body is often paralyzed as my mind races through all the potential pros and cons of every decision, as simple as what to put on in the morning or what to eat for breakfast. I start to hear footsteps and voices behind me. Now I really can't turn around and look like a fool who has been standing in the dark in the middle of the sidewalk. Fueled by a desire to save face more than anything, I decide to keep on walking forward toward the fraternity party. I'll just walk by it like I'm on my way to somewhere else. I recently have been walking aimlessly around campus for hours. It seems to be the only thing that gives my mind temporary relief. As soon as my body stops moving, my mind starts racing with negative thoughts and worries. When I walk, I can just concentrate on putting one foot in front of the other. The only decision I have to make is whether to turn right or left at intersections. I've started to come up with patterns like right, left, right or right, right, left, left, or left, left, right. It doesn't really matter if I keep up with the pattern or not, I'm not headed anywhere in particular. If my thoughts are especially scattered, I will count my steps in between intersections so that my mind will only be filled by numbers and right or left. When I get tired or hungry, I try to find the nearest campus map directory to trace my way back to my dorm. Last week I walked for several hours and came back after the dining hall had already closed, and I didn't eat anything that night.

"Anh! Anh!" someone is calling out my name trying to get my attention. Sometimes when I am walking, I get lost inside my head and don't notice sounds from the outside world, like a biker ringing his bell to let me know he is passing from behind. The person calling out my name now sounds like my roommate, Jessica. I had just been thinking about Jessica. Is this voice coming from inside or outside my head?

"Anh, over here!" the voice calls out again. The night is dark, and the sound of thumping music is so loud that it is hard to locate what direction the voice is coming from.

Finally, I see a shadowy figure rush toward me from the front yard of the fraternity house, where the music is blasting. I can't make out who it is until the girl is almost in front of me. It is Jessica.

"I'm so glad you made it out," Jessica smiles. She is holding a red plastic cup in one hand and gestures with her other hand for me to come join the party. "Come on, let me introduce you to some people."

"No, I was just going for a walk. I'm not here for the party," I reply, sounding so pathetic.

"Oh, come on. You're already here. Just stay for a little bit," Jessica croons in her bubbly tipsy voice that tells me that she has already had a few drinks. I hesitate, so Jessica grabs me by the wrist and leads me toward the group of people she had been standing with. "Hey everyone, this is my roommate, Anh. I told her you can't go to college and not go to any parties. It's part of a well-rounded education," she says, and everyone laughs in response.

"You want some beer?" one of the guys asks as he pumps some foaming yellow liquid from a large silver barrel into a red plastic cup and holds it out to me. I want to say, *No thanks*, but decide it will just be easier to take it and not drink it. Everyone has a red plastic cup in their hand, and I'll just stand out if I don't have one.

"This is my boyfriend, Tom," Jessica says. "He lives here," she nods at the house behind them. "Come on, I'll show you around, it's so different from the dorms." With our beer-filled cups in hand, Jessica leads me into the house, where the music gets louder. The entry hall is filled with people, and the two of us have to push up against people to squeeze by. There is a strobe light rotating in the middle of the dark living room, sending out flickering streams of light around the room where groups of students are moving their bodies to the beat of the music. I am surprised at how many people fit into this house. I have never been to a party like this before. I see couples openly making out and others dancing with their bodies pressed so close together that there is no space in between them. Without really thinking about it, I notice that my throat is dry, and I take a sip from my plastic cup. *Yuck!* I've never tasted urine before, but this frothy yellow liquid, only slightly cooler than room temperature, is what I imagine urine tastes like. It leaves a sour bitter taste that lingers in my mouth even after I swallow it. Jessica notices the look on my face and laughs, "I know, it's not the highest-quality alcohol. Let's get you something a little stronger," she says as she leads me to another room where there is a crowd of people gathered around a table. But instead of red plastic cups, there are small salt-and-pepper-shaker-sized glasses lining the table.

"What do you want a shot of? Tequila? Vodka? Whiskey?"

"I don't know. I've never had a shot before," I answer honestly.

"You've never had a shot before?" Jessica says incredulously. "Well, there's no time like your first. Let's do one together then. I personally like tequila," she says as she walks up to the table and grabs a bottle of an amber-colored liquid. She tells me to hold out two little glasses for her to fill up. "Alright, so you have to drink it all in one swallow," Jessica explains.

"What's it going to taste like?" I ask.

"Honestly, you don't really taste much. It's not bad, better than the beer," Jessica reassures me.

"Alright, ready?" Jessica asks, holding out her glass in front of her. She clinks my glass with hers as she declares, "Cheers," and draws up the glass to her mouth and pours the liquid down her throat all in one continuous motion. I try to keep up with Jessica and awkwardly pour the drink down my throat. I pour it too fast, and some of the liquid dribbles out of my mouth. I start coughing as some of the liquid also goes down my windpipe and I feel a warm, burning sensation in my throat and chest. "Oh my god, what was that?" I ask Jessica. "That was awful!" I holler.

Jessica can't stop laughing. "I love watching someone take their first shot ever. Come on, let's go dance."

It is probably too early for the alcohol to have kicked in yet, but for the first time since arriving at college, I feel a sense of freedom. I am thousands of miles away from my parents. I can do anything I want. I follow Jessica into one of the dance rooms playing hip-hop music, and we join the crowd of moving, sweaty bodies. I'm still feeling a little awkward and out of place, but the dark room, the flashing lights, and the pumping music give me some cover, and I start to relax a little bit. Jessica grabs my hand to get me to start dancing, and I start moving my body to the beat of the music. I still feel ridiculous, but a part of me starts thinking that's maybe the whole point. No one seems to care what they are doing or looking like. An image of my disapproving mother shaking her head flashes into my mind, but I push it aside. My mom doesn't need to be at this frat party with me. I feel sticky bodies pushing up behind me more closely than I'm used to, and I try to wriggle away to make more room. I don't know anyone here besides Jessica, so I stay as close to her as possible. She seems to be enjoying the project of getting me drunk, and every so often tells me we need to go get another shot. I fall into a daze where I just agree with whatever she is saying and take shots with her. It is kind of fun to just lose control. But after my fourth or fifth shot, I've lost count, I start feeling dizzy and wobbly. I can't stand straight, and I'm worried I'm going to fall over or pass out.

"Jessica, I don't feel good. I need to sit down," I tell her.

We sway ourselves over to an old torn couch and plop ourselves down. The whole world starts spinning around me, and I start feeling very nauseous. All of a sudden, I feel an uncontrollable urge to vomit, and I can't stop myself. A rush of warm liquid comes up out of my mouth and spills all over me and the couch. I am appalled. The stench of my gastric juices is now everywhere in front of me. "Ewwwwww, grossss," some girl standing next to the couch says with a look of disgust on her face to her friend. They both back away from me. I am frozen in horror and have no idea what to do.

"Ohhh, Anh," Jessica sighs as she looks at me and the mess I've made. "We gotta get you outta here," she says. Somehow, I make it out of the frat house and back to my dorm room. I don't remember how, or maybe I forced myself to forget how. I wake up the next morning with the worst headache of my life and spend the entire Sunday in bed curled up in the fetal position. Jessica laughs at my hangover.

On Monday morning, I still can't get out of bed. My head is pounding, and a heavy gray fog pushes down on my body, making it impossible for me to get up. I roll around listlessly. I can barely muster up the energy to get myself to the toilet down the hall. I haven't eaten anything in over a day, so I feel weak and light-headed. When I stand up, it takes a minute for the world to steady around me while spots of color drift across my field of vision. I am vaguely aware that I have not showered nor brushed my teeth in two days. I quickly empty my bladder and make my way back to the dorm room and crawl back into bed. When Jessica comes back to our dorm room later that day and finds me still lying in bed, she asks, "Are you OK? Hangovers usually don't last this long."

"I just don't feel good," I reply.

"Have you eaten anything?" Jessica asks with a concerned expression on her face.

"No," I answer. "I'm not hungry."

"Well, you can't survive without eating. I'm going to the dining hall. What do you want me to get for you?"

"I don't really feel like anything."

"Well, I'll bring you back some soup and crackers then. Maybe you should go to the student health center and get checked out."

I reply with a nondescript grunt which neither signals agreement nor disagreement and roll back under the covers to face the wall.

Chapter 39 - Anh

1993

Last week I had a sore throat and headache, chills, and body aches all over, so I missed all of my classes. I feel like shit, like something is "off," but not like an uncomfortable piece of clothing that you can remove. This is an uncomfortable feeling inside of me that I can't escape from. Wherever I go, whatever I do, I don't feel good or at peace. This week I feel better, so I force myself to go to my classes, but I just sit there, my mind both blank and racing, not able to take in what the teachers are saying. In my dorm room, I sit at my desk for hours just staring at my homework, but unable to figure out what to do. In my Organic Chemistry class, I am even more lost than I was at the beginning of the quarter. I have a midterm tomorrow, and I am sure that I'm going to fail it. I can't sleep. I wake up in the middle of the night to try and study, but the numbers and lines and letters start swirling in my head. I force myself to stay up and flip the pages back and forth, trying to drill the information into my brain, but I know it's not making any sense, and my hands start shaking with fear. What am I going to do? I don't understand any of this stuff. I'm going to fail this test tomorrow, and then I can't be pre-med, and my whole future will be over.

It's time to start heading over to the mid-term. I'm not even close to being prepared for this exam, but I have no idea what else to do besides go through the motions of going to class and taking the exam. My hands are shaking so much that I can't even write my name smoothly on the exam sheet that the TA hands out. The exam starts out OK with some simple questions about structure, but when the exam moves into combining reactions, I freeze. I really have no idea how to do this. I can't even pretend to try and work it out. The test might as well be in a foreign language. My body starts breaking out in a cold sweat, my heart starts pounding, and I feel like I'm going to have a panic attack again. I start hyperventilating. I need to get out of here. I haven't even attempted any of the longer-response problems. I'm going to have to turn this exam in more than half-blank. But there's nothing else I can do. I hand my unfinished exam to the TA and rush out of the lecture hall.

Chapter 40 - Anh

1993

"Your performances on this first exam show definite room for improvement," the O-Chem professor says as the TA hands us back our exams. "The curve on this exam was very low. If you are having trouble understanding these concepts, I recommend you come into office hours before the next exam. Remember, your final course grade is based on two midterms and one final exam, so your scores on these exams are each a significant part of your final grade."

I start feeling nauseous. My palms are sweating. The TA hands me back my exam booklet. I see the number 47 circled in red next to the big letter D. My heart sinks. I have never gotten a D in my life before. I am going to fail this class. My parents are going to kill me. I start panicking. The professor starts lecturing on new course material, but I can't pay any attention to what is going on. I can't do this.

I rush back to my dorm. I feel nauseous, so I head to the bathroom and lean over the sink. I close my eyes to try and get the throbbing pulse in my head to quiet, but closing my eyes makes my head spin, making me even more nauseous and light-headed. I am angry, sad, and terrified all at the same time. I don't even know what's right anymore. I lean my head against the tiled wall to steady myself, and I feel my body slump down in exhaustion onto the cold tiled floor, dimly aware that I would normally never allow myself to touch the dirty surfaces in a public bathroom with such abandon. I normally would be repulsed by the imagined germs and splatters of human elimination all around me. But when you yourself feel like shit, you don't care about those things anymore. The flickering fluorescent lights add to the pitiful mood in the bathroom. I can't go on like this anymore. I can't face myself or the world anymore. I can't do this anymore, pretending like everything is fine when it's not. I will die right here in this small bathroom and never have to suffer again. I will release my family from the suffering I have already caused them. They won't have to worry about me anymore.

I reach my hand into my right jeans pocket to find the razor blade I have been carrying around with me, a talisman to end my pain. It is a new blade. I bought it from the ACE hardware store down the street from campus last week when I started having thoughts that I didn't want to live anymore. I told the store clerk helping me out that I needed the razor for an art project. I hold up the blade in my right hand and admire its sharp, shiny newness. I touch the edge of the blade to my left index finger to test its bite. Nothing happens, so I apply more pressure to the blade until I draw blood from my finger. It hurts, but just for a moment. A drop of maroon-colored blood starts to drip, and I take pleasure in its hue and intensity and, for a moment, ponder whether I could paint a watercolor with my own blood. I hadn't known how it would feel cutting into my skin and drawing my own blood, but I find it strangely mesmerizing, as if I'm already in a trance, an alternate existence where my ordinary life no longer matters.

I lift the blade and place it on my exposed left forearm. I clench up my left fist to expose the blood vessels that run parallel to the tendons stretching down the corridor of her arms. For a moment, an image of Shelly from Kahi Mohala flashes through my mind. I remember the multiple marks she had on her forearms, varying in thickness and intensity. I am not one to be wasteful in my actions. I am not trying to make a statement. I want to die. I don't want to be alive anymore. I know I will have to make a very deep cut in order to get to the larger blood vessels underneath to lose enough blood to pass out. An image of my grandmother and mother starts to creep into the back of my mind, praying for me to stop. I push their faces away. It will be better this way, for them to let me go. I read somewhere that I should aim for the radial artery where my pulse can be felt underneath my thumb to have a chance at bleeding enough. I plunge the razor blade with forceful conviction into my skin, flinching at the stinging pain the impact makes, and drag the blade across my flesh with anguish and hatred. My body seems to fight back as the blade refuses to go any further, so I attack again from another angle, again and again, until the blood races as quickly as my thoughts. I want this to end, to be over. I continue to press the blade into my arm until I can't feel anything anymore. I see tiny colored dots start raining down on the screen behind my eyes. I blink to clear them away, but each pounding of my heart makes them pulsate, and the dots grow larger and more colorful until they all collide with one another in a blinding wave of bright white light that drowns me out.

Chapter 41- Anh

1993

My head is still throbbing, as if my forehead has been repeatedly hit by a heavy brick. I reach up to rub the sleepy crusts out of the corner of my eyes and find my left wrist and forearm heavily bandaged with gauze, and my right forearm attached to a plastic IV tube. I am disoriented and confused. I don't remember where I am. The loud rhythmic beeping noise of a machine monitor is the only noise I can hear. Oh shit, now I remember, the sickening fluorescent lights of the college dorm bathroom mirror the sterile room I'm currently in now. Where am I? How did I end up here? I am obviously still alive. I have even failed at killing myself. I quickly look around the room to see if there is any possible way to finish what I had set out to do. As I stir in bed, I hear a rustling of newspaper as a black woman sitting at the foot of my bed turns a page. For a second I am startled and wonder if in fact I did die and went to some alternate dimension. I have never seen this lady before, a middle-aged woman with tortoise shell glasses, wearing a purple cardigan sweater. Is she an angel? The gatekeeper to the afterlife?

"Hello, sweetie, I'm your 1:1," the lady chirps at me.

"My what?" I ask.

"Your 1 on 1. I'm supposed to keep you in my sight at all times to make sure you don't hurt yourself again," the lady calmly replies.

"Where am I?" I ask again.

"You're at UC Davis Medical Center. They're waiting for a bed to open up to transfer you to the psychiatric ward."

My body immediately shoots up. "NO!!! I'm not going back to the psychiatric hospital!!" I yell. The IV needle stabs uncomfortably into my right arm as my body pulls away from the bed. The lady at the foot of the bed quickly stands up to calm me down. "Now, now there. Let's not get agitated or they'll have to give you a shot. My name is Clara, and my job is to keep you safe and alive, and that's what I'm going to do," she says in a forceful tone as she presses a button to request assistance from the nurse's station. In a few moments, several hospital staff wearing scrubs storm into the room. "Is everything OK in here?" asks a stout Caucasian woman with heavy foundation and dark hair pulled back so tightly from her scalp that it looks like it hurts. She appears to be the one in charge.

"The patient just woke up," Clara informs the charge nurse.

"I'll call the psychiatric team to come and evaluate her," the nurse replies tersely. "Make sure she doesn't do anything." The group files out of the room into the hallway.

"Can I use the bathroom?" I ask.

"Yes, you'll just have to keep the door open so I can keep an eye on you," Clara explains.

"You're kidding, right?" I say.

"No, I'm not. You're on suicide watch. I can't leave you alone at any time."

I feel a horrifying swell of humiliation sweep over me. They must think I'm a monster, a crazed animal who has to be kept under lock and key. Why didn't I die? I start ripping the bandaged gauze off of my left forearm to see how bad my cuts are.

"You need to leave your bandages alone," Clara says to me firmly.

"Can't I do anything? Do I need your permission to breathe?" I snap back.

"No, I'd like you to keep on breathing, carry on with that," Clara replies with a smile.

I have a sense of humor, but I find Clara's remark at this miserable moment in my life extremely distasteful. How can she be smiling at me at a time like this? She can't possibly know how demeaning it feels to be tied up to a bed like a chained animal.

There is a knock on the door, and without waiting for a response, a tired-looking young doctor wearing green scrubs and a short white coat walks into the room. His coat pockets are stuffed with papers and a pocket handbook whose title I make out as *Guidebook to the Psychiatric Interview*.

"Hello, I'm Student Doctor Marshall, and I'll be a part of your psychiatric care team. I'd like to ask you a few questions, and then my resident, Dr. Adams, will come in to join me."

He looks very inexperienced and nervous. "So, how are we doing?" he begins.

I don't say a word.

The student doctor tries again. "I read from your admission notes that you were found in pretty bad shape. Your dorm mates found you unconscious and bleeding in the bathroom. Do you remember any of this?"

Again, I don't say a word. I don't want to imagine how I must have looked when I was found lying on the ground of the bathroom floor.

"Were you trying to kill yourself?"

I can't believe this idiot and his stupid questions. Do they really teach you this stuff in medical school?

"Do you still feel like dying?"

Of course I do, you fuckin' idiot, I think to myself. But I don't have the energy to participate in this ridiculous interview. I've already been through this too many times in my life; psychiatrists, mental health workers, social workers, nurses, all asking me how I feel, asking me to rate my depression on a scale of 1 to 10, asking if I have any thoughts of hurting myself or anyone else, if my eyes and ears play tricks on me, and on and on and on and blah blah blah. Why can't anyone really help me? Why won't they just let me die?

"You're 18 and an adult, so we haven't called anyone in your family yet. But would you like us to inform your parents or any other family members?"

My ears perk up. "So my parents don't know I'm here?"

"No, we need to get your consent to speak to them."

"Good, don't call them. They don't need to know about this. Are we done yet?" I ask impatiently.

"I just have a few more questions, if you don't mind."

"I do mind. Can you please leave?"

The student doctor looks unsure of how to proceed. "OK, I will come back with my resident, Dr. Adams," he says as he shuffles out of the room.

"Wasn't he annoying?" I ask Clara. For some reason, I now feel like Clara is on my side, and it is the nurses and doctors who are trying to make my life miserable.

"He was just trying to do his job, and you certainly weren't making it easy for him," Clara answers honestly.

"Well, it's not my job to make anyone's job easy," I answer.

When the door opens again, I know it will be the psychiatric resident along with his side-kick student doctor, who has already made me suffer through his insufferable questions. The resident physician is also Caucasian. He is taller than the student doctor, and his face has bristly several-day-old stubble blanketing his cheeks and chin. His voice is surprisingly soft and gentle.

"Hello, Miss Nguyen, I'm Dr. Adams," he introduces himself. He actually even pronounces my name as accurately as a non-native Vietnamese speaker can.

I am not accustomed to being addressed as Miss Nguyen. I feel myself blush at his gentlemanly formality. The student doctor stands behind the resident, blending into the sterile hospital walls.

"You've had a long night, so I'll make this quick. We're waiting for a bed to become available at one of the local psychiatric hospitals. Hopefully, we'll be able to move you there sometime today. Do you have any questions for me?"

I shake my head in resignation as I prepare for my third psychiatric hospitalization in a year.

It's not until I arrive at Heritage Oaks Psychiatric Hospital that I realize that my golden chain necklace with the jade pendant of *Bá Quan Tề Âm* is no longer around my neck. I panic and ask the nurse behind the counter, "Where's my jade necklace? My grandmother gave it to me."

"They probably have it in storage. No jewelry allowed in here," the nurse answers curtly.

"It's not just jewelry. I never take it off." I start panicking. Bà nội gave me that necklace when I left for college. She said it would protect me in times of danger, and that I could pray to *Bà Quan Tế Âm* whenever I needed help.

The nurse looks like she has addressed this a million times. "It's part of the unit rules. We can't allow you to have any jewelry in your personal possession for safety. But I'll ask staff to make sure they have it locked up safely for when you leave."

I'm now 18, so it is my first time on an adult psychiatric ward rather than the adolescent unit. There is a huge difference. On the adolescent unit at Kahi Mohala, there was at least an attempt to make the surroundings look as inviting as a psychiatric hospital can, with brightly colored walls decorated with inspirational quotes and drawings of animals and flowers. There were board games and DVDs to watch in the community room. At times one could almost imagine that it was some sort of odd summer camp where they give you medication, and you can't leave until the end of the week. The adult psychiatric unit is completely different. There is no denying the fact that one has left the land of the normal and entered a separate and terrifying existence inhabited by disturbing displays of the tortured psyche. I venture out of my room to line up for breakfast and am shocked and frightened to see who my cohorts are. Most of them are much older than I am. There is a tall thin man in his fifties with scraggly unkempt hair who can't stop mumbling to himself. There is an obese woman in her thirties who wears her hair in pigtails and carries a teddy bear in her arms. The other dozen or so patients appear normal enough, the type of non-descript features that, in different circumstances and a change of clothing, would not get them a second glance out on the streets. But they all wear pained expressions on their faces. I wonder how I look in the mirror.

I'm the only Asian patient on the unit. Ever since I've been on the mainland for college, I notice that I have a habit of noticing how many Asian people there are in any particular setting. This is something I didn't do in Hawaii, where there were always Asians around. But here on the mainland, even in Northern California, where there are lots of Asians, sometimes I find myself the sole Asian in the room. Sometimes this distinction makes me feel unique and special. But today, it only makes me feel scared and lonely.

I want to wrap myself back into my grandma's lap and have her stroke my hair and tell me one of the Vietnamese stories she would sometimes tell me, like the one about a clever girl who turned herself into a fly to find what foods the prince liked to eat so she could prepare him his favorite dish, or the one about the benevolent green giant who lived in the forest and changed himself into the form of a large tree to provide refuge for weary travelers who sat and leaned their backs against his trunk. I look into the mirror in the bathroom and do not recognize myself. I have dark circles under my eyes, my hair is straggly and unkempt, and I am wearing ill-fitted hospital scrubs that are standard issue in the hospital. I hate who I see, a crazy, sick girl, someone who is not normal. What happened to the old Anh, the girl who laughed while playing in the ocean in Hawaii?

Chapter 42 - Xuan

1993

I see Anh standing at the edge of an erupting volcano. Liquid lava is spewing violently out of a large cauldron in the middle of a long stretch of rocky black lava fields. Hot, white smoke rises up at various intervals from the ground. The smell of sulfur is strong. Anh is standing alone, staring into the hot orange lava spraying in front of her, debating whether to jump in or not. I desperately try to call out to my daughter, running to reach her, but no matter how fast I run, the distance between us does not shorten. The smoky vog whips around Anh's long black hair as she stares into the bottomless pit of fire. Sprays of fiery magma shoot up from the crater and explode into the air, dwarfing Anh's dark silhouette, like a tiny ant on the edge of a blazing inferno.

I wake up sweating from my dream. "Long, I think Anh is in trouble." I shake my husband to rouse him from his sleep.

"What?" he asks, confused and groggy.

"I just had a dream that Anh is about to jump into a volcano. We need to save her." For a split second, I recognize that my fears sound as crazy as Anh's did that morning she had woken us up to save us from a looming tsunami. I can see the tired expression on my husband's face. "Long, I'm not crazy. I just know that something has happened to Anh, and we need to help her."

Long sighs heavily. Even he is not sure what is real anymore or not. "Let's call her then." He looks at the clock on his bedside table, which reads 5:06 am. It is October. He can't remember if California is two or three hours ahead of Hawaii this time of year. He doesn't quite understand the point of Daylight Savings Time and how it works besides messing people up. Either way, it's not too early to call.

I'm already dialing the number to Anh's dorm room, but there is no answer and it goes straight to the answering machine, "Hi, this is Anh. Leave me a message and I'll get back to you." After the beep, I begin, "*Con gái, me đang lo lắng cho con. Con khỏe không? Gọi mẹ lại.* Daughter, I am worrying about you. Are you alright? Call me back."

"Maybe she's still sleeping," Long says, but my anxiety rubs off on him.

"We need to go check up on her," I'm already swirling into motion.

"Hold on, let's give her some time to call us back. If we don't hear from her today, then we can think about what to do next."

I try to remember the last time I spoke with her. Since Anh has left for college, we call each other briefly on the phone, but I can't remember the last time I spoke to her. I know something is terribly wrong. Something has happened to her. I can't explain it, but a mother always knows.

I call Anh repeatedly throughout the day, but she never picks up or calls back. I have no choice. I have to get on a plane to go see if my daughter is OK. I call Larry at the travel agency to tell him to book me the first flight to Sacramento, which leaves tomorrow. I grab my suitcase out of the closet and start throwing my clothes in. There is no time to think through what I will need, or how long I might stay there on the mainland. But I remember to pack some Hawaiian goodies to give to Anh's dorm mates so they can help me keep an eye on her and take care of her.

"Long, I have to go check on Anh. I can't stay here and do nothing. I need to know if she is OK," I tell my husband. He says nothing but nods his head.

Chapter 43 - Anh

1993

I am discharged from Heritage Oaks Hospital a week later. The doctor there puts me back on Lithium, and my discharge paperwork again has the words *Bipolar Disorder* written as my discharge diagnosis. There are those two horrible words again. BIPOLAR DISORDER. As many times as I have heard them, said them, read them, and been told them, I still cringe at the sight or sound of them. I can't bring myself to fully accept those two words as who I am. Why does every doctor I meet seem so fixated on having me recognize that this is my diagnosis? It seems really important to them that I understand and recognize the gravity of my MENTAL ILLNESS. Another horrible phrase that conjures up no drop of hope or joy from its utterance. The words sound like an unjust prison sentence where one still does not understand what crime one committed to deserve it.

I gave the hospital permission to notify my college residence hall so they were aware of my whereabouts, but I haven't called my parents or allowed the hospital or school to call them yet. A taxi drives me from the hospital back to my dorm on campus. The hospital has laundered my clothes, and I am wearing the same outfit as the day I was sent to the hospital. There are still visible blood stains on my shirt and jeans that weren't washed away, serving as a lingering reminder of what happened. The hospital gave me a prescription for the Lithium that I'm supposed to pick up at my local pharmacy. I wonder how much my roommate Jessica knows? What about my classes? I don't even know what week in the quarter it is. I vaguely remember I had just gotten back my midterm grades. The hospital has made me an appointment to meet with a counselor at the student health center next week. Everything starts to overwhelm me again. I'm scared. I can't do this all by myself, but I don't want to call my parents. They will be so disappointed in me. I feel trapped and paralyzed by my shame and fear. I feel so alone in the world.

When I enter my dorm room, I find my mother lying on my bed with Buddhist prayer beads in her hands. "*Trời ơi!* My God!" my mother exclaims as I walk into the room. "Where have you been? I've been sick with worry! No one here can tell me where you are, they say they can't break your privacy. I don't understand these American laws. I'm your mother, how can I not know where you are?" she cries as she pulls me into an embrace.

"How long have you been here?" I ask, still in shock at seeing my mother's small frame in my dorm room.

"Two days. When you didn't answer your phone, I decide I have to come and check on you myself. Your roommate Jessica has been very nice with letting me stay here," she continues. I flush with dread and embarrassment at the thought that my roommate, and possibly my entire dorm, knows that my mother has flown all the way out from Hawaii to check on me, and has been camping out in my dorm room waiting for me to return. But at the same time, I am so relieved to have my mother here. I don't have to do this on my own anymore.

"How are you doing? You look terrible. So skinny, have you been eating? Where have you been?" my mother attacks me with a deluge of worried questions.

I slump down on the twin bed and tell my mom that I have just gotten out of the psychiatric hospital again. "I got a D on my organic chemistry exam. I don't understand the material. I can't keep up with my classes. I can't be a doctor. I don't know what to do anymore," I let out all at once.

My mother will not let me sulk. "Come on, let's go take a shower. You'll feel better after a shower," and she picks out an outfit from my dresser the same way she did when I was a child. My mom leads me down the hallway back to the community bathroom where I had tried to slit my arms only a week prior. I don't think I can face that scene again so soon, so I stop midway down the hall. My mother notices that I have stopped and comes back to pull me on my sleeve. I pull back and resist my mother's grip. When my mother grabs my wrists more firmly, I scream out in pain from the wounds I recently incurred on myself. "Stop, let me go! You're hurting me!" I yell out. A doorway opens down the hallway, and I see my RA Jeff poke his head out into the hallway to see what the disturbance is all about.

"Anh, you're back. What's going on here?" he asks, trying to assess the situation.

"Nothing," I reply, aware of how awkward this situation with my mother looks. There is nowhere to hide from this mess. "Mrs. Nguyen, is everything OK?" Jeff now directs the question at my mother.

"Of course not. Look at my daughter. She just got out of the hospital, and no one tells me where she was," my mother starts to raise her voice. "You're supposed to be taking care of her here!"

I know I need to defuse this situation, again play the cultural broker between my Vietnamese mother and my American life.

"It's OK, Jeff. My mom just thinks a shower will make me feel better. I'm sorry we're making so much noise," I apologize for the both of us. I take a deep breath and try to figure out how to manage this situation with my mom without losing more face in the dorm. "Mom, why don't we get a hotel room. I'll take a shower there. We both can't stay in my dorm room with Jessica. It's too small for the three of us," I suggest.

My mother doesn't resist immediately, which means she is thinking my proposal over. "OK, that's a good idea. I didn't like showering in the community bathroom either," she admits. I imagine in horror the idea of my mom showering with my dorm mates and walking back to my dorm room in her bathroom slippers and bathrobe. Back in my room, I pack up a small duffle bag of clothes for a few days. My mom takes out a few boxes of Hawaiian Host chocolate macadamia nuts and scenic Hawaiian calendars out of her carry-on luggage before she zips it back up, "Here, for your friends and teachers."

"Thanks," I say as I grab them and throw them on my bed, wondering why my mom packed souvenirs on a trip like this.

My mom ends up staying the rest of the week, accompanying me wherever I need to go – to the pharmacy to fill my prescription, to my classes where she waits for me on a bench outside of each classroom, to my follow-up appointment with the mental health counselor. Each night when I am done with my classes, we choose a new restaurant to try in downtown Davis. When we head back to the hotel room, I do my homework while my mom reads a magazine. She hands me my medication every day twice a day. I strangely feel comforted by my mom's presence, something I haven't experienced before. But I know she's going to leave soon. Her plane ticket back to Hawaii is scheduled for this Sunday.

"You're fine now, Anh. You don't need me anymore. I have to go back to take care of your father. He's probably tired of eating take-out every night," she tells me matter-of-factly. My parents and I do not show emotion with each other, but in this moment, I feel a sense of desperation. I want to beg her to stay, just a little longer, maybe until the end of the quarter? But I have to be strong, or believe that I am strong enough to do this on my own.

"Ok, Mom. Thank you for coming out here to get me back on my feet," I tell her and hug her like a child.

"You'll be OK, Anh. You are a strong girl. You are a smart girl. You can do anything you want," my mother tells me.

Chapter 44 - Anh

1993

After my mom leaves, I struggle to adjust back to the dorm and my classes. I haven't been here long enough to feel like I have enough familiarity to return to. It feels like starting all over again, except now I have a reputation for being "the girl who tried to kill herself in the bathroom." Jessica tries to be nice, but I notice she is distancing herself from me. She has been spending more time at her boyfriend's place, returning to our room every once in a while to grab clean clothes before dashing out again. She's stopped inviting me out with them on the weekend. So mostly I'm left alone. My mind tells me that I'm a failure and that I'll never amount to anything. Got hospitalized in high school. Now hospitalized in college. I'll never have a normal life.

I go through the motions of attending my classes, but it feels like I've lost something inside my mind, some important link that makes everything work right. I can't seem to learn or retain anything, and it's frustrating to be unable to think properly. I used to be a good student. Now nothing is going in. I need to take a break from school. As terrifying as that sounds, I can't do this anymore. I am scared to tell my parents, but I have to.

I call my mom on the phone. I am shaking. "Mom, I need to take a break from school," I tell her.

"What do you mean? Christmas break is not until December," she tells me.

"I need to take a break now. I can't keep going to school. I can't do this," I start crying. I just want my mom to come pick me up and take me home to Hawaii.

"You can't come home now. You need to stay there and go to school," my mom replies.

"But I can't. I can't...." I plead.

Chapter 45 - Anh

1996

I'm stuck at night in a large building. I know in the way that dreamers know that the building is an aquarium. I'm on the third floor and need to find the exit on the ground level to get back to the ocean. It's nighttime, and the new moon is a sliver of light illuminating surfaces just barely enough so that I can make out large shapes and movements, but nothing more subtle. I am barefoot, and there are a few inches of water on the ground that I slosh through. I find a narrow descending path that alternates between stairs and a smooth ramp that wraps around the building and spirals down. I start descending and notice little black crabs and other crustaceans scurrying around my feet. At first, there are only a few of them, and I can avoid the ones in my path, but the lower I descend, the more these creatures increase in number. I have a phobia of insects like ants and cockroaches. Whenever I see one, I get the sensation of them crawling all over my body, and as hard as I try, I can't get the thought out of my head until they are out of sight. The black crabs become more numerous, and they start jumping as well as scuttling across the ground which only frightens me more because now they can jump directly on my body and not just my feet. I feel overwhelmed with panic. I can't keep going down, but I know that the only exit is downstairs. The further I descend, the more of these creatures there are. I don't know what to do. I'm not ready to face these creatures in those numbers yet, but running back up to the third floor will only get me farther away from where I need to go. I need to get to the ocean. I am paralyzed.

I wake up from the dream. I am relieved it was only a dream, but I can't rid myself of the image and feeling of all those little creatures swarming on me. The only way I could escape that nightmare is to face those creatures directly, allow them to crawl all over me as they wish, and walk through them to freedom. But I'm not strong enough to do that yet.

There is a Confucian saying that a lucky man is one who gets to bury his grandfather and father. That is the natural order of life. Older generations pass on, younger generations bury their elders. I knew that one day my parents would pass away, but I had never really thought about that possibility happening any time soon. I am in the living room of my apartment in Sacramento when I get a phone call from my father. I never get phone calls from my father. My mom usually serves as the bridge for communication between my father and me. I hesitate before picking up the phone. I haven't spoken to either of my parents in several months. Communication between us stopped after I decided to go back to California last year. After taking a break from UC Davis my freshman year, I went back home to Hawaii and lived with my parents. I went back to see Dr. Tanaka. I was a mess. I was depressed and felt like such a failure, but Dr. Tanaka helped me realize it was OK that I decided to take a break from school, that there was no rush, that I could take some time to figure things out. My parents let me work at their store and even paid me so I could save up some money. I knew my parents were very disappointed that I dropped out of college, but after a while, they didn't know what to do with anymore, so they just let me be. After living with them for over a year, I finally decided that I wanted to try and move back to the mainland again. I still don't really know where I belong yet, but I needed to move out from living with my parents and move on with my life. I found an apartment in Sacramento and signed up to take some classes at the local community college to see if I wanted to return to UC Davis in the fall or not.

I answer the phone. My father's voice sounds distant and quiet, and I turn up the volume on my phone to hear him more clearly. "Anh, you need to come home. Your mother just passed away," I hear my father choke out. I clench the phone in my hands and press it more closely to my ear. I can't be sure if I heard my father correctly. "What, Daddy? What did you say?"

There is a huge sigh as if my father can't muster up the strength to repeat the horrible words again. Finally, his voice speaks up, "Anh, your mother just died in a car accident. I will buy you a plane ticket to come home."

I listen to my father's words in shock. My mother is dead, and I don't remember the last time I spoke to her.

Airplanes, with their artificial, sterile smell of recirculated air, always make me slightly nauseous. My seat is row 36B. I find my way to the rear of the aircraft, lift my small carry-on luggage into the overhead compartment and settle into my seat. The flight is not that full. It is April, low season, in between spring break and peak summer travel. I wonder whether I will be lucky enough to get an empty seat next to me.

Flight crew members sporting Hawaiian Airlines' latest aloha wear uniforms walk up and down the aisles, helping passengers load their luggage, find their seats, and clear the aisles. I instinctively grab the Hawaiian Airlines magazine from the back pocket of the seat in front of me to see what movies will be offered on this flight.

"Is this row 36?" an elderly Asian man asks me politely.

"Yeah, it is," I reply.

"This is me then," he nods to the empty seat next to me. He stores his luggage in the overhead compartment and places a small black duffle bag under the seat in front of him before sitting down next to me.

"You heading home?" he asks me.

"Yeah, I'm living in California right now, but Hawaii is home," I reply.

"Where do your folks live?"

"My mom just passed away. That's why I'm flying home," I say, and then immediately regret disclosing my mom's death. The plane hasn't even started rolling down the runway yet. I don't want to be stuck talking to someone for five hours about my dead mother.

"I'm sorry to hear that," the gentleman replies with a sincere tone of voice. "When you get to be my age, that starts happening to more and more people you know. I'm 85."

"What were you doing in California?" I ask him, deflecting conversation away from myself.

"I was visiting my son and daughter-in-law and my grandkids. But I have to get back for my senior softball tournament. My buddies are counting on me to play."

"Really? You play softball? That's cool," I reply. I can't imagine my own father being part of a recreational softball league.

"I swear that's what keeps me alive. If I didn't have my buddies counting on me to show up on the field every week, I don't think I'd still be here. My wife passed away 10 years ago, and both of my kids live on the mainland now," the man goes on. The calm manner in which he shares these statements makes me feel that he has come to terms with these life events.

"How often do you visit your kids?" I ask.

"I try to go twice a year. My son lives in California, and my daughter lives in Texas. It's easier and cheaper for me to fly over here rather than have all of them fly to Hawaii to visit me," he pauses, "How old was your mom?"

"She was 46," I answer.

"Oh man, she was young. How did she die?"

"Car accident."

The man lets out a deep sigh and then is silent. There really is nothing one can say after that. I decide to let us both off the hook by putting some earphones onto my ears and excusing myself from the conversation, "I'm going to try and get some sleep." He nods and takes my cue to leave me alone.

I close my eyes, but sleep will not come to me. I am a light sleeper by nature, rarely able to fall asleep anywhere except my own bed and perhaps in the passenger seat of a car if I'm really tired, but I keep my eyes closed to avoid any further engagement. If I can't tolerate talking about my mom for longer than a few minutes, I don't know how I will handle the days to come.

"This is your captain. We are beginning our final descent into Honolulu International Airport, where the time is 9:50 am, and the temperature is a warm 85 degrees with 10-15mph winds out of the northeast. We should have you down on the ground in about 15 minutes. Thank you for flying with us. Flight attendants, prepare the aircraft for landing."

I shift in my seat and gather the empty beverage cups and snack bags from the seat pocket in front of me to hand to the flight attendant making her way down the aisle with a garbage bag. As the plane's wheels touch down on the runway, people on the plane start clapping and cheering, the customary local way to celebrate a safe return home.

"Looks like we made it," the elderly man sitting next to me comments.

I nod without saying a word. I always feel slightly nauseous with takeoffs and landings and often keep the vomit bag close at hand just in case. I brace myself for the dramatic change in temperature, humidity, and smell. As soon as I step off the aircraft and into the open-air terminal at Honolulu International Airport, the muggy heat sacks me like a linebacker.

More subtle than the heat is the distinct smell of rain and plumeria flowers in the island air. It's a smell I haven't found replicated anywhere else, a scent that wraps my body in a familiar embrace. Transitioning from the mainland to Hawaii is a gradual process, physically and mentally. Each day, I feel my body strip away another layer of insulation between myself and the elements around me. My bare skin, which is accustomed to being covered up more on the mainland, exhales with pleasure when I can take off more and more clothes in Hawaii. My physical body acclimates to Hawaii more quickly than my psyche. It usually takes days, and even weeks, for my mind to slow down to the pace of island life. Everything in Hawaii moves slower. The metronome setting on the island is turned way down. People walk slower, drive slower, and speak slower. Days are dictated by the heat and light of the sun's intensity rather than by the hours of the clock.

Jack is now a freshman at the University of Washington. He had flown in from Seattle a few days earlier, so he tells me that he will pick me up from the airport. I haven't checked anything in, so I bypass baggage claim and walk directly out to the arrivals curb to wait for my brother. I take off my long-sleeved shirt and tie it around my waist, and I pull my hair back into a ponytail. I can already feel beads of sweat forming on my forehead and neck.

Jack drives up in a new-looking white Camry and gets out of the car to help me put my luggage into the trunk. "Whose car is this? Where's mom's minivan?" I ask. Jack looks at me with an *Are you serious?* expression on his face, and I realize my mistake immediately. "I rented this car. We need something to get around in, especially this week with all the errands and arrangements." I wonder when my younger brother had become so responsible. I still think of him as a gangly teenager who plays video games with his buddies all weekend.

"Thanks for picking me up," I say to my brother. "Where's Dad?"

"He's at home," Jack answers with a brief response. He's never been one for many words.

"How's he doing?" I ask tentatively.

"I don't know. He hasn't said much," Jack says. We drive mostly in silence the rest of the way home from the airport to our house in Hawaii Kai. It doesn't seem right to ask each other how school and work are going at a time like this. Nothing seems right. This isn't how it's supposed to be.

Jack pulls into our driveway and pushes the garage door opener. The garage is as full of boxes as it was the day we moved in years ago. Both my mom and dad don't like to throw anything away, always saving items that can potentially be used at a future time. They both also love scavenging bargain items at garage sales. I recall how pleased my mom had been to show me the "good as new" outdoor lounge set she and my dad had dragged home from a neighbor's house for free last year. Every time I come home, I find a "new" item added to their growing collection of refurbished household furnishings – a slightly rusty stationary bicycle on the outdoor patio, framed art depicting scenes as varied as the English countryside and Asian portraits of Buddha, and elaborate flower arrangements in large Chinese porcelain vases. Even though my parents can afford to purchase items new, they seem to derive pleasure in finding a bargain and calculating how much money they save buying it second-hand. When I purchase gifts for them for Christmas or their birthdays, they always ask me how much I had spent on them, telling me, "That's too much! Take it back." I've learned to not tell my parents how much I pay for anything.

When I walk into the house, I find my father sitting on the couch watching TV. He looks up at me and nods in acknowledgment of my arrival but does not make any move to get up. I take my luggage into my room. One of the benefits of my parents not throwing anything away is that my room pretty much looks the same as it did when I left for college. My old canvasses, paintbrushes, and art supplies are still in my room. I like painting when I am in Hawaii. But there probably will not be time for painting during this trip. I will only be here for a week, and my mother's funeral is scheduled for this weekend.

The house feels particularly empty without my mother's busyness creating noise in the kitchen and hallways. I walk back to the living room and realize now how awkward it is for me to be in the same room with my father without my mother's intervening presence. Even if my mother was not physically in the same room as us, her presence always allowed an easy escape, I could always say, "I'm going to see if Mom needs help with dinner," and leave. Not that I need an excuse to leave my father alone. He doesn't seem bothered by our long silences in each other's company. He sometimes seems scarcely aware that I'm even there.

I feel an aching tightness in my chest, a familiar feeling that I don't know what to do about. My father and brother have each retreated to their own rooms. I feel sad and lonely. Loneliness is a familiar feeling for me. Perhaps the loneliness is related to the aching in my heart. I look around my room and see the paint canvasses and tubes of paint. Painting always helps me feel better.

I squeeze out dime-sized squirts of yellow, red, and blue watercolor paint from little tubes onto the circular plastic palette. I remember my art teacher Mrs. Rose teaching me that you can make any color from the three primary colors yellow, red, and blue. Infinite combinations and possibilities can come from such simple materials. After setting up the primary colors, I methodically create the secondary colors, orange, purple, and green, by mixing combinations of two primary colors. Mrs. Rose taught me to make a color wheel with primary and secondary colors, setting up the signposts to contain all the colors in between. Some days when I set up my palette of colors, I find myself instinctively drawn to a particular hue on the spectrum. Some days I am more drawn to the cooler end of the spectrum, the blues, greens, purples, and greys. Some days I am compelled to the warmer end with reds, yellows, and oranges. Some days I want to use every color on the surface, and some days I can't find the right color to express myself.

Today I am drawn to green, the color of the jade pendant necklace Bà nội gave me. I go make myself a cup of green tea, rolling its earthy, singed flavor around in my mouth. Green is a deep color, but also a protective color. It doesn't drown me like blue can, nor does it assault me like red sometimes does. I want to dive into its emerald depths and grasp its tender verdant yearnings. I recall my mother telling me about how important rice is in Vietnam and how entire villages spend weeks planting rows of rice seedlings by hand in ankle-deep water paddies. Rice planting is a back-breaking endeavor. One has to step into the mud and carefully place each young rice sprout lovingly into the wet soil underneath the water's surface. Planting rice is like raising children, an investment in the future, a promise of security. Rice is white gold, the sustenance for every family's survival. I mix the varying shades of green in my palette, my paintbrush spontaneously lifting my hand up and directing itself to the watercolor paper. The brush dances across the page with a life of its own, creating a stretching vista of newly planted rice paddies.

I wake up early the next morning, my body still adjusting to the time difference between California and Hawaii. I lie in bed, the same bed I slept in throughout most of my childhood. The window louvers next to my bed let in a soft breeze. The sky slowly lightens, and I listen to the swishing sounds of the palm fronds and the birds chirping and sense how the island around me is waking up too. There are so many different bird sounds – the steady cooing of mourning doves punctuated by the higher-pitched chirping of the red-crested cardinals and the bickering of the noisy mynah birds. Cars occasionally pass by in the background. I close my eyes and let my ears soak in this tapestry of sounds. It is how I want my paintings to feel – layers of experience that speak on their own but also join together in chorus with other elements. I remember Bà nội walking out on our driveway every morning with a bowl of left-over rice soaked in water to feed the birds before her morning prayers. Birds from all over the neighborhood flocked to her side in anticipation of breakfast, even before she threw down the rice. Bà nội did this every morning for years, and it was a sight to see a brood of fifty birds convene on our driveway. Bà nội spread the rice evenly around the driveway so all the birds had room to eat their share. There was enough for everyone and the birds ate cooperatively, none of them fighting or defending territory, behaviors that my grandma did not tolerate. She shooed away any birds that were too aggressive with other birds, and so they learned that if they wanted to eat her food, they had to share.

Bà nội passed away last year after she had a stroke. Now my mother is also dead. I feel so alone in the world.

Chapter 46 - Xuan

1996

We had spoken about it only once. I had told Long that when it came time for me to die, I wanted a traditional Buddhist ceremony to send my spirit off. I wanted to be cremated and my ashes kept in an urn at our local Buddhist temple. I didn't want to burden our family with having to keep my ashes at home, and having to pack it along if they moved. At the temple, my spirit would be tended by the nuns and monks who lived at the temple and who conducted their daily prayers and all the important Buddhist ceremonies on Buddhist holidays. I was practical about it. I had heard rumors of some fastidious Việt Kiều who demanded that their bodies be flown back to Vietnam to be buried in the family graves next to their ancestors. But I knew that when I made the decision to leave Vietnam, I had to give up some of my romantic notions of tradition. At the time, when I had brought up these end-of-life requests to Long, he had dismissed them. I forget how we had gotten on the topic in the first place. Maybe it was right after we attended someone's funeral and the experience was still fresh in my mind. I had asked Long what he would like, but he refused to answer me, dismissing my queries as bad luck. My "wishes" were another way to take care of the family, to unburden them of the task of having to decide what to do. I had always carried the stronger will in our marriage. It was my vision of what I wanted for our family and children that led us to America, to running our business and sending our children to Punahou and college. How would Long and the children carry on without me now?

Even though my body is no longer with my family in the physical world, I will always be with them. I will watch over them. I will protect them. I will communicate with them in different ways now, but I will let them know that I am always there with them. I wish I had more time to say goodbye. There was never enough time to say goodbye when I left my parents in Vietnam, and now again when I left my family in Hawaii. Even though we did not have enough time to say goodbye, I pray that my parents and Long and my children know the love that is in my heart for them, the love that has always been there, the love that will live on. I no longer have tears, but I watch the rain showers fall down on the islands every so often, and I hope that my family will feel those warm drops of water on their faces and look up to the heavens and see me smiling down on them.

Chapter 47 - Anh

1996

My father, brother, and I are dressed all in black. We walk to the front of the room and sit down on the ground in the front row. My auntie and her family are sitting behind us. Thầy Son, the head monk of the temple, along with two other monks dressed in saffron-colored robes, is kneeling before the large statue of Buddha, waiting to start the funeral ceremony. The air smells comfortingly of incense, fresh flowers, fruit, and the various balms and oils that old Vietnamese women like to rub on themselves to ease aches and pains. The small crowd fills with some friends but is mostly composed of regular temple patrons, settling onto their cushions. Thầy sounds a large gong and starts chanting in Sanskrit. He proceeds with a long soliloquy in formal religious Vietnamese that I do not understand. At one point, I hear my mother's name uttered, *Nguyen Thi Xuan*, followed by the names of my father, myself, and Jack – *Nguyen Van Long, Nguyen Lien Anh, Nguyen Minh Jack*. I assume the monk is making it clear who the deceased is and her immediate surviving family members. I had been to Bà nội's funeral, so I know that the most important thing that is expected of me during this long ceremony is patience. I follow along with the chanting, bowing my forehead to the floor, or rising to stand up when everyone around me who is more familiar with the rituals starts to do so. But mostly, I just sit there and remember to periodically shift the weight in my legs when they start falling asleep. I feel like I am going through the motions expected of me, but can't really feel anything besides the sweat forming under my armpits.

I am still in shock about my mother being dead and can't will myself to feel sadness. I half expect my mother to walk up and sit down right next to me and Jack and join us in our prayers. My mom was a devout Buddhist who did her morning prayers at home on a daily basis in front of the family altar. Several hours later, the funeral chanting and bowing finally draws to a close. My father, brother, and I are ushered into a back room where an altar has been set up with my mother's picture. Plates of vegetarian food are laid out in front of her. Thầy continues the ceremony to guide my mother's spirit to the land of Buddha. At one point, Thầy picks up a golden cup filled with holy water and dips a purple chrysanthemum flower into the water, and proceeds to sprinkle the holy water onto a stack of white cloths to bless them. After the cloths are blessed, Thầy sprinkles our bowed heads with holy water and instructs us to tie the white cloths around our foreheads to indicate we are the family in mourning. Thầy then directs each of us to pour Mother some tea into the cups on the altar so she will not be thirsty on her journey. We finish chanting and end the ceremony by lighting incense for the altar.

I hold my lit incense stick and look at the picture of my mother on the altar. I do not know what to say to her. "*Con xin lỗi mẹ*. I'm sorry, Mother. I'm sorry for all the pain and worry I caused you. I'm so sorry." There is so much more I want to express to her but the words don't come to me at this moment, so I put the incense stick in the bowl and bow my head to the floor one more time. The service is done, and the group breaks up to serve the shared vegetarian meal.

During the lunch break, my aunt Thuy sits down next to me. I used to spend more time with Cô Thuy and Uncle Thomas when I was younger, and they would come over during family gatherings. They have a daughter Amy who is a few years younger than me and the same age as Jack. She is currently a freshman at UC Berkeley taking pre-medical courses. All Vietnamese parents can say that their children are pre-med during their first year of college. It's a freebie year where nothing is truly declared except for the wishful thinking of parents.

"*Chào Cô Thuy*," I greet my aunt politely.

"*Chào con*," my aunt replies, referring to me with the intimate term reserved for one's own children or close relatives. "How long are you home for?"

"I have to go back to work at the restaurant next week," I reply.

"So soon? What about your father? Who will take care of him?"

I don't know how to respond. My father is still young, not even 50. He isn't very active, but he certainly isn't incapacitated in any way that requires caregiving.

"Now that your mother is gone, you children need to move back home to be closer to your father," Cô Thuy advises in a tone that is more directive rather than suggestive.

Again, I don't say anything. I hadn't thought about this before, about how my mother's death might affect my life plans. But now that I think about it, my aunt is right. There are tons of decisions that need to be made. Will my father keep the store open? Will he continue to live in our house or move into a smaller place?

"I'll talk to my dad and Jack about it," I say. It is the best I can offer at this point.

Later that night, I mention to Jack about the encounter I had with our Aunt Thuy. "Cô Thuy talked to me at the temple today. She asked if I was moving back home to help take care of Dad," I start.

"Are you?" Jack asks.

I know he doesn't mean anything by it, but a part of me is triggered by his flippant response, as if he is assuming that just because I'm not at university, my life is so transportable. "I wasn't planning on it," I reply.

"Does Dad even want one of us around? He pretty much sticks to himself."

"That's because Mom took care of everything, at home and the store. He's going to be lost now without her," I try to explain, to clarify the situation for myself.

"Well, maybe we should talk to him about what he wants before we make assumptions," Jack says.

We go to eat dinner at the Koko Marina Zippy's, a casual local diner known for its famous benefit fundraiser chili. It's the first time the three of us have had a chance to sit together since I got home.

Jack looks over the menu and asks, "What are you going to order Dad?"

"I'll get the saimin bowl," my dad answers.

"What about you, Anh?"

"I'll get the chili and rice," I decide. The food at Zippy's is by no means fancy, but a few signature menu items hold a special place on my palate reserved for food items I grew up on. Sometimes familiarity and nostalgia are what I want more than the food itself.

Once the waitress takes my order, I decide to start the conversation, "Dad, we need to talk about your plans now."

My father looks up at me with a confused expression on his face. "What plans?"

"What you're going to do now that Mom is gone," I say directly.

There is a deathly silence. He has no response.

"Will you keep the store open?" I try to be more specific.

Again, no response. I look at my brother with a desperate expression on my face, urging him to try a different tack, but Jack looks as lost as our father.

"Maybe it's too soon to think about all of this right now," Jack says quietly, and we are all relieved when the waitress walks up with our steaming plates of chili and saimin.

Chapter 48 - Anh

1996

I am back in Sacramento. It's been a month since my mom passed, and I keep thinking about her. My mom always told me that I would be the one who ushered in a new chapter for our family, that all of the suffering and sacrifice she and my father endured would be worth it for the honor and success I would bring to our family. No pressure, of course. What would Mom say now if she were still alive? That her bipolar first-born daughter, who takes art classes during the day and waits tables at night, is saving the world? Clearly not. The tea leaves and auspicious signs of my birth date and hour must have been wrong. The Vietnamese astrologer probably didn't take into account the time difference between Hawaii and Vietnam, or the fact that Hawaii does not participate in Daylight Savings Time and miscalculated my future. I am not the golden vessel that my mother believed would pour the milk of salvation into our family's parched mouths. I am just another wannabe artist struggling to make ends meet.

"All right, enough of feeling sorry for myself," I say out loud. I decide to go get a bowl of *phở* at my favorite *phở* restaurant. I eat there every week, so most of the staff is familiar to me. The slim, middle-aged Vietnamese woman I often overhear being referred to as Lan gestures me to my usual booth seat near the window. I order a bowl of *phở gà*, chicken noodle soup, which comes out steaming hot from the kitchen just a few minutes later. The aroma of the chicken and ginger steam wafts up into my face, and I delicately dip the spoon ladle into the clear broth for my first sip. The warm broth slides over my tongue, down my throat and into my chest and belly. I feel a warmth in my bones every time I eat *phở*, as if the ghosts of my ancestors are also enjoying the flavorful broth that they no longer have bodies and mouths to taste.

I focus on each bite of noodles and chicken I place into my soup ladle with my chopsticks. I then submerge the spoonful of white noodles under the soup's liquid surface to create a perfect mouthful of noodles, meat, and broth. It is a soothing ritual I repeat over and over until my bowl is empty except for a shallow pool of broth at the bottom. I look around at the tables of other diners eating with their friends or families and feel submerged by a deep wave of sadness and loneliness. I live alone. My mother is dead. Bà nội is dead. My closest family lives thousands of miles away from me. I feel a crushing need to curl up into my childhood blanket and have Bà nội pat me until I drift off to sleep. I don't know how else to soothe myself except with my paints and brushes. I head home and pull out my painting supplies. I feel blue tonight. Deep dark blue. I mix my palette to make the blue as dark as I can without turning it black. I cover the canvas in wide broad strokes to cover up all the white spots I can see. I let the dark blue background dry as I mix up a golden yellow hue. As if in a trance, I watch my hand choose a smaller round brush to dip into the yellow pond and run down the dark background in long thin streaks of tears. When I finish with that, I add some red to the yellow to turn it into orange and then apply strokes of the orange hue to the canvas. Over and over, I choose one color at a time and let my arm direct me as to where I should place the color onto the canvas.

I finally fall asleep in the darkest hour of the night, exhausted from hours of painting layer after layer of color onto my canvas. *My mother Xuan is back in Vietnam. Even though I have never been to Vietnam, I can tell this dream is set in Vietnam because of the striking green rice fields. My mother is wearing a white áo dài, riding her bicycle alongside the rice paddies. The warm afternoon sun lights up her face, highlighting her innocent joyful smile. I am floating alongside her bicycle, as if I am watching her behind a movie camera that is capturing the scene onto film. My mother rides the bicycle past a long stretch of green rice fields until she reaches a forest of trees, and the light grows darker from the shadow of the tall trees. The road narrows into a dirt path that winds deeper into the forest. My mother follows the path that eventually ends at a pool of water. The surface is still, but the bottom of the pool is dark, and nothing can be seen below. On the right side of the pool of water, there is an entrance to a shrine, with red columns arched overhead in a rectangular pattern like a row of enormous staples spaced a few feet apart. Lighting the entrance to the shrine are white paper lanterns floating in the water, each flickering with the soft glow of a lit candle. My mother lays down her bicycle and walks to the water's edge. Without hesitation she enters the water in her áo dài, the water first at her ankles, then her knees, and then her hips as she makes her way towards the shrine entrance and deeper into the water and what lies inside the shrine. She turns and looks back over her shoulder straight at me.*

I awake from the dream. My mother did not say anything in the dream, but there was something inviting and directive about her movements, as if she had been waiting her whole life to show me this path past the rice paddies to the shrine in the water deep in the forest. She brings me into this mysterious and unseen world. I immediately pick up my paint brushes and paint the image of my mother in a white *áo dài* dress wading into the dark pool of water, her slim profile seen from behind as she moves towards the red-columned entrance to the shrine lined with flickering paper lanterns. I can't stop until I finish the painting; there is a force that is pulling me to create these images that I have seen in my dreams. I look at the finished product and am satisfied that it accurately depicts the look and feel of my dream and its power and depth.

It feels like a doorway has opened between me and my mother in the dream world. Now that she is no longer living in this world, maybe she will visit me in my dreams. The next night I have another vivid dream. *I'm standing at the edge of the world. The earth is cracked and dry, and the soil is crumbling away like a landslide. There are children standing at the edges of the land that is crumbling away beneath their feet. I reach out, trying to grab their hands, but I'm too late, and they fall down into the sinking abyss. I'm holding a paintbrush in my hand, and finally a young girl is able to grab hold of my brush. I hang onto the brush tightly and quickly grab the girl by her wrist to pull her back onto safe ground. The girl is about 10 years old, and she stares into my eyes with an intense gaze.*

I wake up and paint a picture of my dream – the young girl staring directly at me, the grey scene of the world collapsing around her.

One of the classes I am taking at the community college is about teaching art. I've been thinking about becoming an art teacher rather than continue waitressing to pay the bills. I want to work with kids. Today our art class is going to visit a place where our teacher Janice volunteers from time to time. I have no idea where we are going until we drive up to a place with a sign that reads "Asian Pacific Community Counseling" over its entrance. Janice leads us into a conference room in the clinic and tells us more about the clinic and the class she teaches there.

"I started volunteering here several years ago after my brother was a patient at this clinic," Janice explains. "My brother has schizophrenia, and he still comes here to get his medication and counseling. My family didn't know what to do after he was diagnosed with schizophrenia. We didn't even know what that word meant. It was so scary seeing my little brother change into someone I didn't recognize. He started becoming very aggressive. He wouldn't leave his room, and every time my parents tried to get him to come out to eat, he would fight them. This went on for a long time at home before my parents took him to see a doctor. They put him in a psychiatric hospital for weeks, where they gave him medication that made him like a zombie. My parents didn't like seeing him that way, so they stopped giving him his medication when he came home. But then he went back to the way he used to be and ended up getting hospitalized again. It took several years for my brother to get better, for his doctor to find the right medication, and for my family to trust the medication. This clinic has helped us so much. They are a clinic that helps Asian families deal with mental illness. Asian families deal with mental illness differently. They don't talk about it. There's too much shame and misunderstanding about it. Families don't want others to think that it's their fault that their child has a mental illness, so they don't get help for it, but that just makes things worse."

I cling on to every word Janice is saying. It has never occurred to me before that my family's Vietnamese culture somehow affected my own experience with bipolar disorder.

Another student asks Janice curiously, "So how did you end up teaching art here?"

"It was really by chance. Even though my brother was doing much better than he was before, it made me sad that all he did was sit at home watching TV all day. He had always been so creative and loved art and drawing before he got sick. When I encouraged him to spend more time getting back to his art, and bought him the sketch paper and drawing pencils, I was surprised at how much he enjoyed it and how good his drawings were. His illness and the medication seemed to take so much away from his personality, but his drawings were still filled with that special part of him that I knew existed before he got sick."

I feel a strong urge to share with the group my own similar experiences with mental illness and the relief and release I feel when I paint, but I can't find the courage to do it. I have never told anyone outside of my family and my doctors and nurses about my diagnosis. It feels like a shameful secret I have to hide from the rest of the world. But here is my teacher, talking about her brother's illness so openly. Without even thinking about it, I blurt out, "How does your brother feel about you talking about his illness with others?"

Janice smiles kindly. "That's a good question and something that took my family some time to decide. My brother doesn't mind me sharing his story, but my parents don't like me talking about it so openly. They still don't talk about it with any of their friends or our relatives, and people have learned not to ask them about it either. It's like an unwritten 'don't ask, don't tell' policy in our community."

I think about how I would feel if Jack started going around talking to all of his friends about his older sister with bipolar disorder and how many psychiatric hospitalizations she's had and how she dropped out of college. I would kill him if he did that. I better call him later and let him know exactly how I feel about my privacy.

Janice goes on to explain the format of her class at APCC. "I run this art group here once a week. It's very informal. Anyone who is a client of the clinic can show up, and all supplies are provided. Each month we choose a different modality to work with so clients can experiment with different mediums. Some clients are drawn to one more than the other, whether it's painting or ceramics or music or poetry or photography. We keep technique to the real basics. I just want to provide people with an opportunity to express themselves. I truly believe that art is a way for people to heal themselves, to connect with their true self, regardless of their diagnoses. Art can be a way for them to see themselves as unique expressions, each one providing a unique and worthy perspective of the world. We have art shows where clients get to display their work, and people can purchase them, also giving them a tangible sense of their ability to contribute to society. It's my goal that we can spread groups like this all around the country, to bring our brothers and sisters, aunts and uncles who have mental illness out of the shadows and back into the light."

Janice leads our group into a spacious conference room and instructs us on how to help set up the class. Today's modality is watercolor paints, and I feel comforted by my own familiarity with this medium. My fellow classmates and I tape down butcher paper on the desk surfaces to protect them from paint and water spills. We then set up individual painting stations with a palette and dabs of color and brushes, and a container of water and paper towels to clean their brushes. We set up 10 stations in a circle around the room facing the center. Janice tells us that attendance varies in this class. Sometimes only one person shows up, sometimes seven people show up. She never turns anyone away.

This particular day three people show up for the art class. I still can't believe there are Asian patients who come to this clinic for mental health issues. One is a short, fair-skinned girl in her twenties wearing her hair cut short in a boyish cut who looks very anxious. She walks with a slight limp, and her leg muscles appear atrophied. The second is a young, stocky man in his late twenties or early thirties. He wears dark glasses that he keeps on for the duration of the class and constantly turns around, looking behind him as if he is expecting someone to jump out and attack him. The third participant is a middle-aged woman wearing a floral pattern blouse and loose-fitting skirt. All three of the participants look especially nervous with so many new people in the room.

Janice tries to put the group at ease. "Hi, Mai. Hi, John. Hi, Vang. It's good to see you all. I have some special visitors today from American River College. These are my students as well, and I brought them here today to see what a special class we have. They will mostly be observing our class, but feel free to ask them for assistance with anything. If they can't help you, they'll grab me. OK, let me take out the pieces you all were working on last time. You can continue working on them today or you can choose to start a new piece. Remember, we are focusing on color and how we can make color darker or lighter depending on how much water we add to the paint." The three students appear stiff as boards, frozen into their seats as Janice places the pieces they were working on from the previous class in front of them.

I hang back and don't approach the students. I can tell they are nervous about us being in the room and all those eyes on them. I try to sneak glances at the flat boards with watercolor paper taped onto them that Janice places in front of Mai, John, and Vang. I am struck by how different each person's piece looks. Each had started with the same three dabs of red, yellow, and blue on their palettes, but Mai's piece is primarily purple and blue in hue, while John's work is composed of varying shades of green, and Vang's painting is awash in bloody red streaks. Janice is an unobtrusive teacher. She allows the students to work on their pieces in silence, but also walks slowly amongst them, stopping to provide a few gentle words of encouragement or praise to each of them. I watch how the students relax into their bodies as they begin dipping their brushes into the water and mixing colors. Their initial frozen stiffness at the beginning of the class has melted away like the dabs of paint on their palettes as they each work in their own worlds. A feeling of lightness bubbles up in me. This is so cool. I want to come back here and help Janice teach this class. I want to paint with them. The forty-five-minute class passes quickly, and soon it is time to clean up.

"Janice, can I come back here next week and help you with the class?" I feel an excitement, an energy bubbling up inside me that I haven't felt in a long time.

"Of course, we'd love to have you, Anh. Please do come back," Janice replies kindly.

Chapter 49 - Anh

1996

I come to the Asian clinic on Mondays to help Janice run the art class. "I haven't seen you around before. You must be new here. My name is Derek. I'm a therapist here," a cute Asian guy who looks slightly older than me introduces himself in the clinic lunchroom with an outstretched hand. He seems genuinely friendly and confident, unlike a lot of other Asian guys I've met before. He is easy to talk with, I can see why he would be a good therapist. I feel simultaneously at ease as well as intensely curious about him.

"I'm only here on Mondays when I help Janice with the art group," I reply.

"Oh, you must be Anh then. One of my clients is in that group, and she always tells me how much she loves it," he says.

"Really?" I ask, flattered that he already knows me by name.

"Oh yeah. She used to be so depressed and never left her house for anything, and now she leaves her house to come to your group and to the art store to buy supplies. I've noticed a real improvement in her since she started the art group," Derek continues.

I feel embarrassed. I sometimes wonder whether I am doing the art class more for myself rather than the participants. I desperately want to find my path. I've felt adrift and lost since dropping out of college. I've been enjoying the art classes I've been taking, but unsure where it will all lead.

After our initial first meeting, Derek and I look for each other in the breakroom during lunchtime, hoping to run into one another. Conversation flows easily between us. I feel comfortable talking to him, like a close girlfriend who I'm also kind of attracted to.

"I'm working with this teenager that's really frustrating," Derek tells me one day while we are eating lunch.

"Yeah? How come?" I ask.

"She's so smart and does so well when she takes her medication, but then she always stops taking it and ends up back in the hospital again. It's so tiring," he complains.

"I bet she's tired of it too," I respond.

"Well, then she should just take her medication!" Derek says emphatically.

"It's not that easy just to take it," I start feeling defensive, wondering whether I feel safe enough to disclose more of my personal history to Derek. "There's probably a lot more behind not wanting to take it."

"Yeah, I know," Derek says. "But it's just so hard when I keep seeing her falling back down each time. It's like she's fighting herself or the fact that she has an illness."

"You're probably right," I say. I have never thought about it that way before. Have I been fighting myself and my mental illness? Honestly, in the past year, I haven't even been thinking about my bipolar, hoping that I could stuff it away in some closet that I never had to open again. After I dropped out of UC Davis and went back to Hawaii, I saw Dr. Tanaka and took my medication for a while. But then I felt fine, so I stopped taking it when I moved back to California. I haven't thought about Dr. Tanaka in a while. I wonder what she would say to me now? Would she still tell me that I had bipolar disorder and that I needed to get back on my medication? Being here at this Asian mental health clinic these past few months brings back all these old memories about my past back to the surface. Where did my bipolar go? Did I really have it? Did it go away, or is it just hiding in some dark corner of the closet, waiting to come back and ruin my life again? Even thinking about this feels scary. That if I look for it, it might just find me again.

I am paddling slowly in a canoe. The ocean water is calm and glassy like a lake. The boat moves forward through the water, cleanly cutting a path toward a distant shore. Instead of a canoe paddle in my hands, I am holding a paintbrush. I curiously lean over the side of the canoe and let the brush trail in the water beside me and watch with amusement as the brush leaves behind its own small wake as we glide along. The water beneath my paintbrush starts to swell up, cresting in size and volume. I apply pressure to the brush to keep it from jumping out of my hand from the force of the water underneath. I hold it steady near the water's surface, and the water starts curling up behind the brush into a large smooth wave. The wave crests skyward and then over me, creating a spacious water tunnel for me to travel through. I have always wanted to ride inside the tube of a wave, and here I am, riding inside a wave created by the paintbrush in my own hand. Instead of traveling down the open face of the wave as it opens up, in this wave, I am traveling deeper and deeper into its origins, the place where it begins, the source of its power.

I wake up from the dream knowing there is a connection between the dream and my art and my bipolar illness. Even though I'm scared of my illness, a part of me seems to know that the place inside me where my paintings come from is the same place where my bipolar lives. They come from the same source, except one stream leads to art and one stream leads to psychiatric hospitalization. By cutting myself off from my bipolar illness, have I cut myself off from my own creative source? In that moment, I see flashes of vivid images run through my mind, a series of paintings that are a mixing pot of Vietnam and Hawaii – images of Vietnamese villagers wearing conical hats and colorful garments harvesting fields of pineapple, images of slim Vietnamese women wearing beautiful *áo dài*, riding graceful ocean waves on long boards off the waters of Waikiki, the tails of their *áo dài* fluttering behind them in the wind creating their own wave forms above the water. I have a Vietnamese soul that was born and raised in Hawaii. I feel energized to create a series of paintings to express my love for my Vietnamese heritage and the shores of Hawaii that gave our family refuge. I remember the series of water paintings I was working on in my senior year of high school before I had my first manic episode four years ago. A part of me is scared that painting another series will bring my bipolar back, but I know that I can't close myself off from my painting out of fear. My art is a part of who I am, just like Vietnam and Hawaii are a part of who I am. I haven't decided if being bipolar is a part of who I am yet. My mother had always hoped I would write a new chapter for our family story. Can I still bring honor and good fortune to our family in a different way?

Chapter 50 - Anh

1997

I am running toward the water. My body feels strong as my legs move me across the pavement. My arms pump in rhythm and coordination with the rest of my body. My breathing is full. I am working hard but have enough breath to feel fluid. As the water comes into view, I start removing layers of clothing as I run. It feels liberating to pull off my bra and shirt and underwear and feel the warm air blow directly onto my bare skin. There is a dock jutting out into the water in the distance. Without any hesitation, I run down the wooden platform and at the end of it, I jump into the air above the water. As I am about to hit the surface, I draw my legs together to enter the water in a pencil dive. I plunge into the grey-green depths of the water, my lungs filled with enough breath to carry me deep into the bottomless green. When I finally reach the nadir of my trajectory, the buoyancy of the water starts to push my body back up to the surface. I throw my head back and let my face lead the way to the light. With a final breath, I break through the water's surface with delight. I glide to the dock and climb up the ladder, letting the water drip down my warm, naked body glistening in the sun.

I come home to observe the anniversary of my mother's death with my father and brother. Every year on Memorial Day, thousands of people line the shores of Magic Island to release paper lanterns adorned with the names of loved ones who have passed on, and messages they want to send to them. The ceremony has roots in Japan, but as with everything else in Hawaii, the ritual is adopted by the local culture and evolves into a fusion of different beliefs and practices. I want to honor my mother at this ritual.

After my mother passed away, my father sold their store in Waikiki and went back to his job as a parking attendant. He was not cut out for business like my mom was. Running LX Hawaiian Fashions was too much for my father alone. Every day at the store was a constant reminder of my mother's absence behind the cash register, on the telephone, organizing the merchandise, pushing the postcard stand back inside the store every evening when it was time to close.

I pull out an *áo dài* dress I had tailored for myself in California for this occasion to honor my mother. I unclasp the buttons on the dress to slip it on. It fits perfectly on my body. I pull on the white silk pajama bottoms. As I draw the long zipper up the length of my leg, it glides smoothly, drawing together the two seams of the material into a custom fit that feels at home on my body. I feel beautiful. I feel Vietnamese. I finally fit into my own *áo dài* dress that was made for me.

At sunset, I make my way to the shore at Magic Island. The orange sun is drawing its final arc toward its resting place behind the mountains. I cradle a paper lantern boat I made for my mother. Fresh tears run down my face and drop into the salty waters below. My chest aches with the emptiness of my mother's absence. I will no longer be able to wrap my arms around her small frame. My mom always slipped out of my embrace before I was quite ready to let go. Invisible tendrils stretch between us, resisting the separation. I try to let the memories of my mother drip through the sieve of my heart like slow-moving thick honey. How did my mother have the strength to leave her family and motherland and carry on with living? Had she ever been able to truly let go of this loss? Or had the ground she was rooted in simply been ripped away, leaving her adrift to find refuge somewhere in the great expanse of the Pacific Ocean? We were lucky to find refuge in these warm shores of Hawaii to give us new life.

I breathe in the salty ocean air and follow its course through my lungs to each cell in my body. I stand calf-deep in the ocean and feel the warm waves lap against my legs. A light passing rain shower falls briefly down from above, and then the sky clears again. A feeling of gratitude for the simple gift of being alive to experience this moment washes over me. Standing next to me, another family gently lays down their paper boat, sending afloat their loved one on the water's undulating surface. My father and Jack and I place my mother's boat alongside the stream of other vessels. A swell of emotion lifts up inside me. The temperate wind brushes across my wet face and neck as gently as god's tender exhale. This is aloha. The horizon stretches off into a hazy intersection between the blue-mauve waters and the glowing peach sky. The sun finally slips beyond the curve of the earth, sending forth its warm outstretched rays that leave nothing from sea to sky untouched.

Epilogue

Đời cha mẹ ăn mặn, đời con khát nước.
When the parents' generation eats salt, the child's generation thirsts for water.
– Vietnamese proverb

Westerners might interpret this proverb as a way to blame one's parents for all of one's misfortunes. But the Vietnamese parent and child know that the saying speaks to the truth that parents and children share an unbreakable bond with one another, passed on through the waters of our ancestors and descendants in one continuous stream of life. Even after death, life continues on through our children.

The saltwater composition of our tears is the same as seawater. The people of Vietnam have experienced enough loss, trauma, and sorrow to shed an entire ocean of tears. It is the grief of our tears that turns salt water into fresh water for new growth and life. Each generation can transform our salty tears of grief into pure spring water to nourish the next generation.

ACKNOWLEDGMENTS

The writing and birthing of this book into the world has been an act of love and healing. As with all births, it would not have happened without the lives of all those who came before me. This book first and foremost is an honoring of my ancestors, and their lives that live on through me and my children. I would especially like to name my maternal grandparents Nguyễn Thị Đà and Trần Văn Lừng, and my paternal grandparents Phạm Thị Nhân and Nguyễn Đình Phúc, and the generations that came before them. My own life would not have been born without the love and sacrifice of my parents Trần Thị Kim Cúc and Nguyễn Đình Khang, for whom I am eternally grateful. My father passed away in April 2022, and I know his spirit continues on through his children, and my two children Sebastian Minh Gutierrez and Penelope Lien Gutierrez. I love you Sebi and Neli. Family is where we come from, and it is the legacy we leave behind. Love and thank you to my family - Grandma Lê Thị Lam, Auntie Thọ, Uncle Bruce, Auntie Nina, Uncle Vang, Auntie Sue, my sisters Jackie and Rosie, my brother Billy, my cousins Christina, Victor, Stacy, all of our beautiful children in the next generation, and Noe and the Gutierrez family that welcomed me in as one of their own.

I have been blessed with many teachers and mentors along the way that have each played a role in my development. Thank you to every teacher that has ever taught me. I can not name all of you here, but I was your student, and I will pay forward the lessons I have learned. Thank you to Josh Reppun for being the first teacher to encourage my writing, told me it was OK to not fit in, and to use my unique voice, Dr. Tyronne

Dang who introduced me to the world of medicine and serving the Vietnamese community, Dr. Larry Zaroff who taught me about kindness and humanity in medicine, Dr. Shirley Feldman who was whip-smart and believed in my work, Dr. Hendry Ton who mentored and inspired me as a Vietnamese physician, Dr. Alan Koike, Dr. Francis Lu, Dr. Russell Lim, Dr. Sufen Chiu, Dr. Nang Du, and Dr. Kiet Truong for championing culturally competent care for our Asian-Pacific Islander community, Dr. Susan Flynn for teaching me that love is what truly heals, by loving me, Dr. Paul Yang who introduced me to spirituality in psychiatry, Dr. Malia McCarthy and Dr. Harry Wang who were my "parents" in my development as a child psychiatrist, Dr. Kristina Schwerin and Dr. Chris Larsen who helped me open my private practice, all of my colleagues, Asian Pacific Community Counseling family, and all of my patients and their families who were truly my teachers by trusting me with their stories and their lives. I could not have learned how to be a physician without them.

My life has always been divinely guided and I am very blessed to have met so many wonderful souls that have been a part of my journey along the way. Thank you to Bruce Logan and Elaine Head, who in many ways have been with me since the beginning of the journey of this book, by inspiring me with their own book *Back to Vietnam: Tours of the Heart*, and who since have been my ambassadors of kindness and goodwill across the Pacific Ocean between Vietnam, Hawaii, and the shores of our hearts, Florie and Wild Women Rising for awakening the wild woman in me, Aja for activating my multidimensional gifts, Rebecca Wildbear and the work of the Animas Valley Institute for reconnecting me to soul of the Earth and her wisdom, the members of my Water Keepers Community who honor the spirit of water, Marcia O'Regan for holding me to my soul's highest potential, Siobhan Gannon for such deep healing, Melissa Bow and Quyen Truong for reading early versions of the manuscript and encouraging me with their feedback, Mr. Đẳng-Giao for helping me to reach readers in the Vietnamese community, friends and fellow writers who gave their time to read my manuscript and write me a review, all the ladies on the island of Divinely Prosper and the wonderful women writers at the Unbound Press, which has been a divine collaboration. My life would not be as joyful and complete without my dear friends who see me for who I truly am, and Jeff my soul mate, for our love. Thank you to Nicola Humber at Unbound Press for creating this special womb space for women writers, Emma Mulholland for making the birthing process so easy, Leah Kent for your intuitive beautiful designs, and Jesse Smart for editing my manuscript in all the ways it needed.

It has been said that if you can only utter two words your entire life, the words "Thank you" would be enough. I know I have left out many names that deserve to be named. I ask for forgiveness in advance. But please know that I truly have love and gratitude in my heart for every person and connection that has touched my life, no matter how small. Thank you. Thank you reader for reading my book. Thank you. Cảm ơn. Mahalo.

ABOUT THE AUTHOR

Elizabeth Nguyen, MD was born and raised in Honolulu, Hawaii. Her parents were refugees from Vietnam who arrived in Honolulu in 1975 at the end of the Vietnam War. She received her BA from Stanford University in Human Biology, her MD from Northwestern University, and her Psychiatry Residency and Child Psychiatry Fellowship training at UC Davis. She started her career in community mental health, with specific interests in cross-cultural psychiatry, the intersection of spirituality and mental health, and the healing power of water and the natural world. She currently lives in Davis, CA where she is in private psychiatry practice and makes frequent trips across the Pacific Ocean to the islands of Hawaii where her body and soul feel most at home.

Of the inspiration behind and the intention for Aloha Vietnam, Elizabeth says:

"There is so much trauma and healing in the human ancestral lineages, and water, art, and storytelling help us in becoming whole and natural again. This book is my love offering to the land and the people of Vietnam and Hawaii, and the vast Pacific Ocean that connects them. It is my hope that it provides beauty and healing to the trauma and suffering that has come through generations of loss and the struggles of mental illness."

You can find her online at:
www.multidimensionalpsychiatry.com and
www.waterkeeperscommunity.com

Elizabeth Nguyen, MD
multidimensionalpsychiatry
waterkeeperscommunity

Made in the USA
Columbia, SC
07 January 2023